CHILDBIRTH COACHING GUIDE (This is not medical advice; always follow your doctor's instructions)

Your Role as Her Birth Coach

Real labor is your cue to take charge; be confident, calm and make sure everything she needs gets handled. Be her capable protector who is going to help her get through this. Remain positive for her no matter how you are feeling.

☐ **Get ready early:** Once labor starts, check your lists and make sure everything is packed and ready to go.

☐ **Make the calls & check her in:** Call the doctor, handle the paperwork and any hassles at the hospital.

☐ **Manage communications:** With the nursing and medical staff, ask questions and get answers.

☐ **Present your birth plan:** To the labor nurse on each shift and remind them of its core elements.

☐ **Support her:** The nurse will come and go and shifts will change; you are the main member of her support team.

☐ **Listen to her:** If she is shy about making requests, ask her what she wants – regularly.

☐ **Encourage/reassure her:** Build her confidence, tell her she is doing great, how proud you are of her, and that you love her.

☐ **Indulge her:** In any way possible. Pursue her every request regardless of whether you think it is necessary.

☐ **Take her best shots:** It is the pain and frustration talking. You are helping her blow off steam (and pain).

☐ **Manage friends/relatives:** You may need to politely ask visitors to wait outside. The nurse will help.

☐ **Be flexible:** Deal constructively with new events that may require a change in course.

☐ **Handle any tough decisions:** Keep her informed but keep in mind that she may not be lucid when in labor.

☐ **Watch her face:** When you present her your baby to hold for the first time.

Be Her Advocate

Only you will know what she really wants, and you need to express her needs to the staff. Intervene and, if necessary, be assertive, such as asking that the anesthesiologist or doctor be paged. Do not lose control and become obnoxious; this will scare her and you will become the problem. Keep her informed and let her wishes guide your actions.

She Needs You

Your presence alone is a major comfort to her as she experiences the surreal, often excruciating experience of birth for the first time. She needs your familiar voice and touch and knowing you care for her more than anyone else.

WHEN IT IS TIME TO GO

Once her contractions are 40-60 seconds long and 5 minutes apart for an hour, most doctors will tell you it's time to go to the hospital (earlier if the drive is long). Call her physician, report her status and follow instructions. Call immediately if her water breaks, or if there is actual bleeding, or if her pain does not subside between contractions. If she or you are concerned about how things are going, err on the side of caution and call early, but try to avoid going early to the hospital because being sent home is very frustrating.

DRIVE HER TO THE HOSPITAL CAREFULLY

Check your list and load the car. This is no NASCAR event; drive as smoothly as possible since sudden moves and even small bumps on the road are a shock to a woman in labor. An easy drive also helps mom stay calm and focused.

Doctor Name _____

Dr. Phone _____

Hospital Phone _____

Other _____

Instructions on when to call/go to hospital:
_____
_____
_____

© DadsAdventure 2008   Available at DadsAdventure.com

When She Goes Into Labor

False labor can be very frustrating, but it will pass. Labor is real when her contractions steadily intensify and do not go away when she gets up and changes position. She may also develop low back pain; once the real thing kicks in there is no mistaking what it is.

WHAT IS HAPPENING

Labor is causing her cervix to gradually efface (thin out) and dilate (open up) to "unplug" her uterus to enable the baby to pass into the birth canal. Her water may break and she may pass the mucus plug.

Mucus Plug — Cervix — Birth Canal

EARLY LABOR

Labor averages 15 hours for first time moms, with about half spent at home which is more comfortable than a hospital room. Encourage her to relax, sleep, talk, walk, take a bath (get a quick shower yourself), watch a movie, or snuggle (these last hours together before you become parents can be very special). Try to get her mind off her labor and save her energy for later as it gets more intense. Encourage her to eat (e.g., a banana), drink fluids and go to the bathroom.

PERIODICALLY LOG HER CONTRACTIONS

The key to handling early contractions is to get her to ignore them as much as possible (also delay use of labor techniques until they are necessary). So don't log them all, just 4-5 in a row when she thinks they have changed. Use the log attached and write down the start times to the second, and then time and write down the length. The time from one start time to next is how far apart they are (see example). If you are math challenged, try contractionmaster.com.

HELP HER DEAL WITH PAIN

Pain Medication: Yes, No, Maybe?

Her method for dealing with pain is her call. If she wants an epidural, urge that it be provided as early as possible and don't expect it to eliminate all her pain. Use basic pain control techniques to help her. If she wants to go without pain meds, support her in every way possible. If she has trouble tolerating the pain early in labor, encourage her to consider medication because it may become much worse. If it is late in her labor, remind her how far along she is and encourage her to stick it out. This way she will know she gave it her best shot. Then follow her wishes, and if she requests an epidural, ask that it be administered immediately. Also ask about the point when it would be too late for her to obtain one.

Take a Few Pictures, Monitor the Equipment, But Focus on Her

Count her through contractions; let her know when the monitor indicates they peak. Ask the nurse what to look for so you can alert her if necessary. Not a good time to get fascinated with machines, though. Sam with your role as cameraman; take a few pictures but keep the focus on mom.

Engage Her Directly & Passionately

☐ Get hands-on; hold her gently, caress her head, massage her, get whisper-close to her face.
☐ Talk her through each contraction; pace her breathing, tell her when it peaks, when it is done.
☐ Start breathing with her and if she falters, encourage her to "breathe with me, there you go, stay with it now, hang in there, it's starting to peak, it's on the way down, that's it baby."
☐ You may need to get face-to-face to get her focus back. Calmly but firmly, tell her to "look at me, stay with me, I love you and am going to help you get through this, now breathe with me."
☐ Once a contraction ends, help her relax. Ask her if she wants anything else, and depending on how it is going, suggest a different position, breathing pattern, or whatever you think might work.

Time for Intense Coaching

If she becomes distraught, desperate, despairing, highly stressed, or experiences a high level of pain, it is time for you to take your coaching to the next level to help her regroup. This will be intense, so get in close, stay with her, and do whatever you can that may work. Never give up on her; if you do, you can no longer help her. Project confidence and firmness in your manner, touch and tone of voice. Remember, she will be feeling birth pain for the first time and may react in unexpected ways.

Silence Can Be Best At Times

She may find an intense, inward focus is her best way to get through strong contractions, and telling her how to breathe may break her concentration. If you sense this is the case, just back off.

Call In The Reinforcements

If she gives up, tell her you love her, how tough this must be for her, and "we will get through this!" Ask for help from the nurse, who can encourage her, determine her progress, suggest something, or help coach. Tell mom that "your baby is on the way." Always remember she will get through it.

THINGS TO TRY

Soft Music May Help In the Initial Hours

Research has indicated that soft music can reduce mom's perception of pain in the first hours of active labor, so set her up to listen with an iPod or CD player.

Massage Is Her Strategy of Choice

Massage will help her relax between contractions as well as speed labor along. Ask her where to rub or ask the nurse for ideas. Keep at it but pace yourself.

Techniques From Childbirth Class & Elsewhere

Use the techniques you learned in childbirth class and try anything else you (or she) thinks might work.

☐ Set up her room with pictures, scented oil, etc.
☐ Help her establish a focal point.
☐ Take her mind off the labor by reading to her, or engaging her mind in other ways.
☐ Try slow dancing with her arms around your neck.
☐ Ask for an exercise ball.
☐ Let her squeeze your hand during contractions.
☐ Suggest she change her breathing pattern.
☐ Encourage her to grunt like tennis players.
☐ Suggest she lie on her left side, or other positions.
☐ When she is pushing, work with the nurse to hold her legs in a position that helps her bear down.

Dealing With Painful Back Labor

The hard back of the baby's head may be pushing on mom's spine. Ideas to reduce her pain:

☐ Try a position that moves the baby's head away from her spine, like mom on her hands and knees.
☐ Changing positions, pelvic rocking or squatting may help rotate the baby and relieve the pain.
☐ Strong massage or pushing to create counter pressure where it hurts. Try tennis balls in a sock.
☐ Hot packs, ice, or a warm bath or shower with the water targeting the pain may help.
☐ Ask the nurse or doctor for ideas and support.

WELCOME TO SERIOUS MANHOOD

Conducting *Boot Camp for New Dads* for almost two decades and raising four children of my own has given me plenty of time to think about what it means to be a father and what it takes to be a dad. Many men fail their children in many ways, and in my day job of working with Trauma Centers across the U.S., I see some of the saddest results in pediatric intensive care units. I ask myself, "what causes a man to fail as a father when virtually every one of us wants to do right by our child? What do men who are just starting out need to know to do their best?"

I think we all face a common hurdle in doing what is right; the notion that fatherhood is emasculating, that becoming a father, with all that diaper changing, babysitting, nurturing, etc., somehow make us less of a man. A father-to-be recently nailed this with his question: How can I have a baby and still be a man?

I think I may have answered this question when I wrote the following for a movie called *Daddy Boot Camp* that was optioned by the same studio that did *Triple XXX*, *Anger Management*, and *Black Hawk Down*. The script called for the Boot Camp coach to give a graduation speech to the new dads, and the writer asked me to take a shot. This is what I would like to say to all new fathers who give it their best:

It takes a man to raise a child. Staying up with a crying baby, working without sleep, changes in our relationship with our mates, often needing to earn more and still do our part at home, rarely time for ourselves, the demands of protecting, guiding, and being a role model to our children.

There are times one must dig deep for strength just to get through, and at times having failed, we must dust ourselves off and get up and try again. And again, if necessary.

Among fathers, the real man walks his crying baby night after night even though exhausted, cares for his baby's mom with little in return, helps his son get to college when he didn't go himself, volunteers as his daughter's coach even though he doesn't know what to do, fights to get help for his sick child from a system that doesn't care, forges ahead with a troubled teenager when he doesn't really have a clue.

Fatherhood presents all of us, no matter our size, strength or income, a unique opportunity to show what we are made of, to be a hero to someone we love. Hard to imagine, but you are going to be a hero; the tough kind that takes decades, with times when you may want to walk away. The kind that takes the special courage of having to answer to no one but yourself. The kind that takes care of his child no matter what.

When she is born, she will wrap her tiny hand around your little finger – and before you know it, you will be wrapped around hers. He will fall asleep on your chest, warm and secure in your arms, with no one else to look after him and protect him like you will.

As she learns to walk, you will be there to catch her when she falls.
When he learns to talk, his first words will include daddy – or something close enough.
When she scores a goal, she will look right at you and smile.
And when he graduates, he will grab you in a bear hug and not say a word.

On behalf of all veteran dads, I wish you strength and fortune in meeting the challenges ahead and experiencing the best that life has to offer. Welcome to the adventure of your life.

Welcome to serious manhood.

> *You have an idea of what it is to be a dad and then being a dad happens to you. You have NO idea.*
> — *Veteran Dad*

WE ARE ALL IN THIS TOGETHER

One of the great things about Boot Camp workshops is that we get men from all walks of life. You'll see a young truck driver orient a corporate lawyer on the fine points of burping a baby, or an African American veteran showing an Asian rookie how to change a diaper. And when those babies start crying, we all react the same way. At Boot Camp, men of different cultures, ages and incomes quickly find mutual respect when working together to learn how to care for their children. We recently found the same when we conducted a training program to set up *Boot Camp for New Dads* (AKA "Hit The Ground Crawling") in England with a group of teen fathers in Liverpool (check out a clip on DadsAdventure.com). It is clear that we fathers are all in this together.

We Are Brothers

I have six brothers, and I can tell you that it feels very good to have other men respect and understand you and give you a hand when you need it. Over the past eighteen years, Boot Camp has worked the same way: we respect and look out for each other, extend a hand through our advice and sometimes just listen. We are all brothers in a sense.

Let's Reach Out to Each Other

When you see another new dad, ask him how old his baby is and whether he is getting any sleep. Then with a nod to his baby, tell him "nice job." He will light up; you will have made his day. A quick glance of understanding to the father struggling with a crying child, will strengthen his patience. Ask the guy on the plane or in the next office about his kids and you will make a friend. You will also find that what goes around comes around.

Give A Helping Hand to the Next Guy

When you connect with new fathers you know or meet, don't be shy about telling them what you have learned as a dad. You can also pass on what you have learned to other rookie dads by taking your baby to a Boot Camp workshop or posting your comments on DadsAdventure.com. Ask your questions as well, and hear what the experience of other fathers has taught them. Get some fathers you know together for a hike or trip to the car show and try to make it a regular habit.

Look Forward To Organized Activities With Other Dads

Sports generally start at age 5 (soccer, T-Ball) and offerings like flag football and lacrosse are continually being added. The YMCA's Guides and Princesses father son/daughter programs also start when your child is about 5. They all provide great opportunities for dads in coaching, leading and contributing, and you should look forward to the camaraderie that can develop as dads work together and learn from each other. Some men who have never played sports themselves end up becoming their child's coach and the neighborhood's as well. This can be a great way to go as a dad.

Let's Make the World a Better Place for All Our Children

You do your job, and your brothers, cousins and friends (and eventually your own sons) will notice and follow. If we all do our jobs, we will be leaving the world that our kids inherit in better shape than we found it. Not a bad legacy.

Fatherhood presents each of us a tremendous opportunity. Let's help each other make the most of it.

When men facing a common challenge get together, a locker room bond quickly develops and they come away inspired.
- Veteran Dad

FINAL WORDS OF WISDOM FROM THE GUYS

Your Baby Will Provide You a New Source of Strength

Given the opportunity, your baby will grab hold of your heart, motivate you to do your best, and add dimensions to your life that for now are unimaginable. Trust it will happen, look for opportunities to make it happen and then take full advantage when it does. As one smoking father trying to quit said, "every time I wanted a cigarette, I picked her up and looked in her eyes, and it was like she was asking me to do it for her."

Turn Your Buddies into Uncles

You need your buddies for balance in your life. Most men don't make friends easily, and after a baby arrives we tend to lose touch with those we do have. After being tied up at home before and after the birth, your friends get the idea that you are out of circulation. Jump back in by showing up with junior. After a few times asking, "can you hold her for a minute," they'll be reaching for her all the time. Show them how to feed her with the bottle, rock her to sleep, and of course how to do the tricks you have taught her. They will call to ask if you can bring her over to play.

Make Your Fatherhood Your Own By Bringing Your Baby into Your World

New fatherhood has been described as a roller coaster ride in which just hanging on is a challenge. Once things settle down, start charting your own course as a dad rather than just getting swept along by the demands you face or even the course set by your wife. Make it your own by introducing your child to the things you enjoy, like sports, the outdoors or car shows (with her in a backpack), painting or music (they are naturals), or develop some new interests you can share.

Take Pride in What You Do

Becoming a father is the ultimate rite of manhood for those who step up to the challenge. You won't find a more rigorous trial, and whether you succeed or fail is entirely up to you. As men, at some point in our lives, we want to know what we are made of, and as a father, we get our chance to find out. Periodically assess how far you have come as a dad and the commitment you have made to your child. Accept any mistakes as the price of trying, and take pride in all that you do.

Engage Your Spirituality

We dads should gather all the strength we can muster to meet the challenges along our path, but one source many of us overlook is our spiritual dimension. Whether we report to a God through a formal religion, simply believe in God or even Karma, a new baby personifies the most wonderful of creations and the very meaning of life. Consider calling on all available spiritual powers to help you do your best as her dad.

Trust That You Will Get To Where You Want To Be As a Dad

Like new moms, we also struggle to adjust to our new responsibilities and go through a process of self-discovery. While we fathers have a longer transition to parenthood, ultimately we become different people as well. Tougher, better, more fulfilled men. As long as you keep trying, especially after tough periods that can take the wind out of your sails, you will get to where you want to be as a dad.

Introduce Him to Your Father

Grandfathers are often last in line, so make it special when it is time to introduce your baby to your own father. Take your baby and ask your dad to follow you alone into another room, show him how your baby likes to be held, and ask your dad – father to father – what he remembers about his newborns. Try it with your father-in-law too.

"   *It's the most frustrating but most rewarding experience.*

- Veteran Dad

GREAT ADVICE FROM EXPERIENCED FATHERS

This is my best shot at synthesizing the advice the veterans at Boot Camp have offered over the years:

☐ The tremendous changes experienced by new moms can be very tough and confusing, and they in turn can be very tough on new dads. If this is happening to you, keep in mind you have lots of company. In fact, part of the basic job description for new fathers is to serve as mom's punching bag. As men, we are built tough, and if we understand what's happening, we can take it.

☐ The basic challenge you face is not changing diapers or comforting a crying baby, but working with your wife to form a new family. The pressures and demands that new babies bring often place a serious drag on your relationship just when you need to be working together. It is essential that you take the long view and form a team approach that benefits the baby, strengthens your relationship and provides long term stability for your family.

☐ Fatherhood is about growing up and accepting responsibility. For most men, this takes time, so cut yourself some slack, but keep moving forward. We all have an instinctual desire in our heart to do right by our child, but stuff gets in the way. Those who do the job understand the rewards are well worth the sacrifices; those who do not don't know what they are missing.

☐ Loving your child at first sight, or at any time, is not automatic. Get involved, give it time, and keep up. "She came out looking like my mother-in-law; it took time". Babies can be a wonderful source of joy and fulfillment, but they can also be boring, frustrating and irritating. How it all adds up is up to you. Prepare for the worst and take advantage of the best. The key is developing confidence before she arrives, and jumping in with both hands once she does.

☐ You bring your own unique strengths to the job of parenting, and you should be confident that you are fully capable for caring for your baby. Develop your understanding and capabilities as a father, and focus on making the most of the practicality, creativity and stamina you bring to this task.

☐ We learn best from men who are doing the job. Talk to your brothers, friends and other dads around you. You can blow off steam, gain some perspective, and get some new ideas. If you connect and share experiences with other fathers, you will be surrounded by men who will help you do your best.

☐ While fatherhood is forever, it occurs one day at a time, and some days will be better than others. You are going to make mistakes, and each new day presents an opportunity to take another shot. It is a tough transition, and you must be patient with your baby, your mate, and yourself.

☐ Next to a sense of confidence, a sense of humor is what will get you through the tough times. Laughing beats crying, so work on it, and help mom with hers as well.

☐ Parenthood often comes at a time in a man's life when he has to work 60-hour weeks; some dads believe they can make up for lost time later. You can't, so make sure that you do spend time — even if it's just an hour a week — alone with your baby now.

☐ If you don't take care of yourself, you won't be in a position to take care of your new family. Keep in mind that your good health and mental well being is essential to all of you.

☐ Develop unique things between just you and your child, like a secret handshake, that make you both feel important. Start with a funny face that lets him know it is playtime, progress to high fives, and as he grows, proceed to more complex maneuvers. It reminds him and you that you are special to each other, an inseparable team.

> **"** *You have two ears and one mouth, so listen to your children twice as much as you tell them what to do.*
> — *Veteran Dad* **"**

THE 20 BEST TIPS FROM *BOOT CAMP FOR NEW DADS*

We started *Boot Camp for New Dads* in 1990 and in 1995 compiled the top ten tips for dads to be from the experienced dads in our workshops. They have stood the test of time and are as follows:

1. **Trust your instincts.** A little experience will quickly turn you into one of the world's leading experts on your own baby.

2. **Learn from the best.** Ask the hospital nursery personnel to show you how to change, swaddle and bath your baby.

3. **When it comes to mom, be patient and positive.** Communication and support are the key. She'll love you for It.

4. **Stand your ground.** Let no one push you away from your baby. Not your mother-in-law, your mate, your boss, no one.

5. **Learn as a family, just the three of you.** Keep "help" in the first weeks down to what is needed lest it become interference.

6. **Your baby is portable.** You can take your baby anywhere. Don't get caught up in fretting about what you can't do.

7. **You will get frustrated.** Step back. Think. Count to some high number. Think again, and so forth.

8. **Make eye contact.** Babies talk with their eyes. You will see!

9. **Relax and enjoy the ride.** Make it a daily habit to play with your new baby, check out her tiny little feet, have him fall asleep on your chest, etc. It's the little things that count the most.

10. **When times are trying, remember they too will pass.** Before you know it, you will have a teenager on your hands.

More Tips From Boot Camp Over The Last Decade

Since then we have heard from many thousands of experienced fathers in our workshops and have culled out their best tips to help you get a good start:

1. **Set the tone you are "here to play" and change his first diaper** – ask the nurse to walk you through it.

2. **Becoming a father has highs and lows.** Getting informed and ready for whatever might happen is the best thing you can do. The lows can be tough, but the highs make it all more than worthwhile.

3. **Spend time alone with your baby away from mom.** This time on your own is when you build your strongest connection with your child.

4. **There is no one right way to be a dad.** Every baby, mom and dad is unique. Lots of choices need to be made and you – along with mom – are the one to decide what works best for your new family.

5. **We learn best from fathers who are doing the job.** Talk to your brothers, friends and other dads around you. You can get stuff off your chest, gain some perspective or even get inspired.

6. **Most of what you need to know comes naturally.** Change his diapers, rock him to sleep, give him a bath, and within a week or two you'll start feeling like a natural.

7. **Fatherhood is about sacrifice, honor, and fulfillment as a man.** It takes time to adjust, so cut yourself some slack but never stop trying.

8. **Before she arrives, you will have little idea how important you will be to your child**, or how important she will be to you. Just know that there are great reasons us dads give it everything we have.

9. **No matter what happened during pregnancy** — whether or not you played Mozart to the baby or rubbed mom to be's back enough, remember **the rubber hits the road when the baby is born.** What happens after that is what counts.

10. **And** especially in these over commercialized, hyper compulsive child rearing times - **don't sweat the small stuff.**

" *It's just nice to get some advice from regular guys.*
                                                    - Rookie Dad
"

10 ADVENTURES FOR 0 TO 3 MONTHS

1. **Her Favorite Mug:** For the first few weeks a baby's vision is fuzzy. She'll fixate on things that are about a foot from her eyes - like your face when you hold her. Let her check out your mug and grab your nose. Place a picture or toy with contrasting colors in his line of sight to catch his attention; then move it back and forth slowly so he can track it.

2. **Monkey See, Monkey Do:** Get close to her face and smile. Around four to six weeks she will start smiling back. Many babies will imitate your facial gestures, so open your mouth, widen your eyes, and of course, stick out your tongue. Even if she doesn't, keep trying, because this game can hold her attention for a long time.

3. **Airplane:** Hold your baby with both hands— one under her bottom and the other cupped on the back of her head and neck. Hold her up in the air and let her fly around slowly and gently. Always firmly support her head and keep it higher than her bottom.

4. **Pull-ups:** Put him on your lap facing up, place one finger in his hand so he grabs on, and pull it up a little. Then put another finger in his other hand so he grabs on with both hands. Pull him up just a little (keep his unsupported head on your lap), and then let him down and repeat.

5. **Baby Calisthenics:** Games involving limb movement are possible at this age, but you'll have to do most of the work. With your baby on her back, gently pull her legs up toward you and then side to side, talking to her the whole time. Do the same with her arms.

6. **Jumping Jacks:** With your baby on her back, raise her arms over her head and then put them down. Then take one arm and gently cross it over toward the opposite shoulder. Repeat with the other arm. While you're doing it, count off the moves (a one and a two and a three and a four).

7. **Walking at a Month:** Their walking reflex is very cool. Supporting him with both hands, stand him on the bed and lean him forward. He will slowly raise one foot as if to take a step, and if you move him forward, he will take another. Another amazing feat to show the guys.

8. **Belly Time:** Now that we put our babies to sleep on their backs to help prevent SIDS, they have less opportunity to develop their upper body strength by lifting their heads and pushing themselves up with their hands. So give him plenty of belly time while playing and he will be the first and fastest crawler in his Mommy & Me group.

9. **Kiss Her Hand:** Give her a chance to touch you in return. Letting her know how wonderful she is, and how all her moves are amazing will tell her you delight in her attempts, and she'll do it more and more. Tone it down when she turns 5; you don't want to embarrass her.

10. **Sit on Your Chest:** Lie down on your back with your baby sitting on your chest facing you. Let him explore your face. Enjoy his intense concentration as he checks everything out. Be careful because he may grab your nose and try to remove it.

Elvis!: Bruce Springsteen, Radiohead, The Killers or whatever you like. Once he starts rocking out, you can take him on tour to grandma's house. Got a comedy act buried deep? Time to drag it out. No matter how bad you are, he'll think you're the best.

 When she wakes up in the morning, she gets all excited when she sees or hears me. You can't buy that type of feeling.
- Veteran Dad

8 Adventure

OTHER DADS SHOW YOU HOW

If you think about the adventures you want to have together, whether it's teaching him to fish, surf, work on cars or name the stars, you are not only more likely to do these things, you realize how much you have to look forward to with your child. To help you get going, we offer examples of other dads' adventures with their kids:

Racing

It may not seem an obvious choice to invite your daughter to ride along while you compete in a Baja ProTruck race at Pikes Peak, but Rob Reinertson had his 17-year-old daughter Christine as his co-driver for the 15 minute competition. After relaying information about upcoming twists and turns to her father while being jostled around in his race truck, Christine said the experience was one of the highlights of her life.

Surfing

Paul Solotaroff's son Luke is afflicted with a rare genetic syndrome similar to autism. After years of struggling to find an activity to stimulate Luke, Paul came across the idea of rehabilitative surfing. Just minutes into his first wave, Luke was exhibiting joy rarely seen by his parents. Now both father and son are learning to surf, spending time together, and Luke is experiencing significant improvement in motor skills, social skills, and behavior.

Building Boats

Paul Rollins has been rebuilding boats for three decades, but now he's doing it with his son (22 at the time of the article) Paul Jr. Working out of two boat barns (one of which, Paul Jr. lives in) just feet from Paul Sr.'s house the two spend their days restoring and building boats and it's Paul Sr.'s wish for Paul Jr. to one day take over the family business.

Skiing

On the urging of her father John, 5 year old Anne Rostenberg would walk up a small hill near her home in an effort to get used to her skis. 35 years later dad and daughter are still skiing together. Both say that it's their yearly ski trips that have helped to keep them so connected. Taking a cue from the Rosterbergs, Sean McCarthy is already skiing with his 3 year old Julia, although she gets a tether and harness that's controlled by dad.

Karting

Enrolling his son in a short go-kart course to see "where he fell with it" Mike Distler could not have predicted that his son Woody would immediately begin putting up race times one might expect of an older teen or adult who was familiar with racing. At age 11, labeling Woody a "prodigy" isn't a stretch of the imagination. Indy car racers Michael and Marco Andretti, and Sam Hornish Jr. are all former kart racers who have made good on their early success.

Cooking

Wayne Brachman – professional chef and author of several books on cooking- spends many nights a week shopping for groceries and cooking with his two daughters. Wayne's goal is to get his daughters thinking about food: expanding their palates; knowing where their food comes from; what it takes to prepare; and how it affects them. At the ages of 8 and 5 his daughters are already doing a significant portion of the cooking (under supervision), and have already developed a greater sense of the wider world of food (that is, beyond PB&J and Mac & Cheese).

Computers

David Moses and his 5 year old daughter Zoe have been playing on computers together since she was 2. They work together on both hardware and software. Zoe has her own computer and is so comfortable with the ins and outs of computing, that she trains the other children in her class.

Survival Training

Sometimes there is an unexpected bonus from teaching your child about the outdoors. When 5-year-old Hannah Klamecki was swept away in a river from the island she and her grandfather were swimming she made some important decisions that helped her survive. Her grandfather drowned after he was swept away, but Hannah, who had floaties on, had been exposed to the outdoors by her father. She drank water from the river and ate berries to survive the two days in the woods.

> *I put a small surfboard on the wall next to the crib and bath time is for learning to paddle. She mostly just splashes, but she's only 3 months old.*
> *- Veteran Dad*

MAKE YOUR FATHERHOOD AN ADVENTURE

Get Ahead Of the Curve

Babies are a lot of work and caring for them can be very boring, especially if you decide to wait until they learn to "play catch" to have fun. Get ahead of the curve by turning mundane tasks with your child into mini-adventures, and building up to bigger ones as they grow. This will get you both ramped up for the magical years of ages roughly 3-10 (longer for girls) when they think that you are the greatest person on earth. Do this and they might stick with you through their teen years (dream on).

With a couple of decades ahead of you two, the sky is the limit when it comes to having fun and adventures together. So now is the time to start planning and doing.

- Check out the 0-3 Months Adventure list on page 8-C.
- At 6 months, the child you want to teach to surf can start swimming lessons.
- A 2 year old is a great assistant for gardening, and they are amazed at how tall and fast corn grows.

Dad's Adventure isn't necessarily an Indiana Jones style excursion through an abandoned tomb with your toddler strapped to your back. Although with appropriate safety measures, it could be.

Take a Hike

Get a good baby backpack carrier that goes easy on your back, and start with short trips to lengthen his attention span and get yourself in shape. That way when your hike together turns magical, with him jabbering away about the cool rocks you hand him, you and he will be comfortable and want to keep going. You won't need a diaper bag for short hikes, but a jacket for weather changes, sunscreen, a hat and a small First-Aid kit will keep you well prepared.

Re-live Your Own Childhood Adventures & Plan On New Ones

What were the things you liked best about your own childhood? They make great traditions with your own child, so start early and invite your own dad to join in. Camping and fishing are classics, and you can start her off in the backyard and bathtub.

Girls Can Do Anything Boys Can Do

Picturing our sons playing in the NFL comes naturally, but girls, well, they do girl things and then fall in love with some guy with questionable motives. Our instincts tell us to rough-house with our sons, but to hug and protect our daughters. So you can see it's easy to shortchange our baby girls right from the start (same with our boys when it comes to hugs). So start her early. She definitely benefits from rough-housing with you; research shows that girls whose fathers engage them in sports grow up to enjoy better fitness, stronger self images, and healthier, lasting relationships later on in life with men (on that note, teach her a martial art).

> **"You may think a baby means you will no longer be able to do the things you like to do.**
>
> **Actually, a child can provide the opportunity to do what you always wanted to do."**
>
> My first OB said this to us guys and it turned out to be true. Learning to ride horses with my daughter, play paintball with my sons, being another daughter's pitching coach, taking all my kids to explore some part of the world when they turned 14; all in addition to camping, fishing and starting backpacking at three.
>
> - Greg Bishop, Author

Organize Outings With Other Dads

New dads stuck at home with a baby will jump at an invitation to join you and your baby on a Saturday morning at a coffee house and then an outing. A father in Marin, California started a group that goes hiking with their babies in backpacks (A.K.A. "Grateful Dads"), and so can you. Nothing like getting together with friends, co-workers, guys from childbirth classes, etc., to trade stories, learn new techniques, blow off steam, and create a "nursery in a locker room" setting.

 When guys are connected to their children early, there's more likelihood that they'll stay connected.
- Veteran Dad

Notes

Notes

MAKING A FAMILY WITH A SPECIAL BABY

Avoid The Blame Game

As with any situation that feels out of our control, a baby born with a disability or illness can trigger in us a need to blame something or someone. Often mothers take on the guilt for not having produced a perfect child, even if the cause of the disability runs in the genetics of the father's side of the family. The point here is that no matter what, blaming another for the situation you are in will only delay the necessary process of getting to know and love your child and at the same time could cause a fracture in your marriage.

Make Your Relationship Stronger

You might hear that a child who is ill or disabled will make you and your partner feel closer, but this is not necessarily true – especially at first. The added demands impact every area of your life. Work, friends, family relationships, finances, and self-concept are just a few of the areas that take a hit. So the question becomes: what can you do to help your relationship weather the storm? The answer is, a lot.

- **Don't isolate.** A baby who is different makes for parents who are different from other parents. It is easy to feel cut off from the support that you need as a couple if you can't share common challenges with parents who understand where you're coming from. Search your community for parent groups that are geared to parents of children with special needs.

- **Seek professional help.** One of the keys to pulling together with your partner is sharing your perspective with someone who is experienced with the situation you are going through. This kind of support can create a safe environment to explore the issues and emotions associated with caring for your baby as well as your relationship.

- **Validate your partner.** Every mother needs to know she is a good mom. This concept is tantamount as it applies to the mother of a child with special needs. You can strengthen your connection with your partner by giving her positive feedback about her skill as a mom. Spend time on a regular basis pointing out all your child can do, see, and hear instead of only what they can't.

- **Practice self-care.** You will be the most help to your family if you take care of yourself. Take a bit of time each day to do something you enjoy. Even 30 minutes will strengthen your ability to cope with stress and help you keep a positive perspective.

A Deeper Kind of Love

If you hang in there and stay focused on what is important, the chaos surrounding your unexpected circumstances will give way to loving your child for who they are. Parents who successfully navigate these turbulent waters find that they come to a place where they are able to celebrate their child's smallest victories and accomplishments. This is where you're headed and when you get there you will know it because your heart will be filled with pride, humility, and love. Start by spending as much hands-on time as possible with your baby and learn how to care for him.

The Loss of a Baby

The only outcome more unthinkable than a child born with a disability is one that is still-born or dies shortly after birth. Although you don't want to dwell on this possibility, it is important to remember that most hospitals have loss and grief support for parents dealing with this circumstance. The process usually includes on-going individual counseling for both parents as well as groups for parents who have lost a baby.

This form of support typically has two goals. One goal is to help the family work through the myriad emotions associated with the death of a baby and the other is to help the family incrementally evaluate their readiness to have another child. For some couples this is a relatively quick process and for others it can take a while. In the end most couples who have lost a child at or shortly after birth go on to have another pregnancy that results in a successful outcome.

When she was born, it was obvious something was wrong. It came as a shock and I was totally unprepared.
                                                                        - Veteran Dad

BABIES WITH SPECIAL NEEDS

There are many books and resources that address the issues surrounding babies with special needs. Our purpose here is to touch on a few of the key points that have specific implications for fathers.

There are over 300 categories of birth defects and developmental disabilities listed in the National Birth Defect Registry. Most types are rare; for example, hypoplastic left heart syndrome affects about 3 of every 10,000 babies, and cleft lip with or without cleft palate affects about 1 of every 1,000 babies.

From autism to scoliosis, however, one in 33 babies in the U.S. is born with some sort of birth defect. While it is inconceivable to most people that their baby might have a disorder, it does happen.

Sometimes parents find out about a disability, such as Down syndrome, during pregnancy. At other times, there's a dramatic surprise, a cleft palate or heart problem, which surfaces at birth or later on.

It goes without saying that babies born with disabilities will require extra care. However, the extra care required is not usually as demanding as the psychological process we must confront as parents of a baby with special needs.

Receiving the News

Whether during the pregnancy or after the birth, the news of a birth defect shatters our fantasy of what it will be like to be a dad and leaves us facing a vast unknown. Dads who have confronted this challenge agree - your baby needs you now more than ever. Your baby must have everyone in her corner, advocating for her and seeking to understand how best to care for her.

Be prepared for the fact that, especially at first, even your closest friends and relatives may not know how to help you deal with your new situation. They may ask hurtful questions, offer bad advice, or generally just shy away until they figure out how to handle their own emotional responses.

It is critical that you and mom stick together. Talk to her early and often so you both know what is going on with each other. Anticipate that bonding and loving your child will be harder, which in turn can lead to serious guilt.

Give It Time

It is likely that your vision of fatherhood includes an image of you and a child that runs, plays, and laughs. You may see yourself in the future passing on your wisdom to this child that represents the continuing generations of your family. If your child has a disability, this vision may require realignment.

Coming to grips with your child's new realities does not happen quickly. The initial shock of finding out usually gives way to a long period of denial. Somewhere within these two stages the flight-or-fight response is triggered, sending some dads running from their family, trying to escape this daunting challenge.

Running, of course, is not an option for you. In fact, by hanging in there and giving it time, you will be building a bond with your child that is deeper than anything you imagined prior to his birth.

Circle the Wagons

The most effective way to focus your worries and concerns on something productive is to start assembling your resource team. This will include friends, family, medical experts, and some form of emotional counsel. The best place to begin is the hospital where your baby was born. Often the staff that is treating your baby will be your first resource for basic medical advice about your baby's particular condition and how to care for your baby properly. The hospital's social worker will know of resources in your community that can be helpful in supporting you.

7 Family

> *I learned that even when a baby isn't capable of interaction, the baby still needs the dad's hold and touch to balance the woman's hold and touch. There's something that brings a calmness to the baby. When it's just all mommy, the baby tends to fuss a lot more.*
>
> *- Veteran Dad*

IMMUNIZATIONS

National Network for Immunization Information
66 Canal Center Plaza , Suite 600 , Alexandria , VA 22314
Phone: (877) 341-6644; Fax: (703) 299-0204;
Email: nnii@idcocioty.org
ImmunizationInfo.org

Immunize.org
Information and immunization schedule.

Immunofacts.com
Facts about immunization safety.

INFANT/CHILD DEVELOPMENT

ZeroToThree.org
Information for parents about child development in the first three years with an emphasis on brain development.

NLM.nih.gov/medlineplus/infantandtoddlerdevelopment.html
Information and links cover developmental mile stones to age twelve.

LHJ.com/home/Stages-of-Child-Development.html
Early child development and growth information. Printable child growth chart.

INFANT CPR

American Red Cross Headquarters
431 18th Street, NW, Washington, DC 20006Phone: (202) 303-4498
Information on infant CPR classes.
RedCross.org/services/hss/courses/infchild.html

University of Washington
Instruction sheet on infant CPR to print out.
Depts.Washington.edu/learncpr/infantcpr.html

MARRIAGE COUNSELING/ROMANCE

Counsel-Search.com
Home of the National Directory of Family and Marriage Counseling. Use it to find a Family and Marriage Counselor in your area.

Marriage.about.com/od/adviceandselftests/qt/needhelp.htm
Online support. Links and resources.

MarriageAdvice.com
Find articles on a variety of Marriage subjects.

NEW MOMS

BabyCenter.com/pregnancy
BabyCenter's pregnancy section is a comprehensive guide to new mom issues.

MayasMom.com
Maya's Mom is popular social networking site where moms can get advice from other moms and share their own.

Momscape.com
Ideas, projects and information for parenting with spiritual support.

SheKnows.com
A network of information and resources, including recipes, information on going back to work and health issues.

PRODUCT SAFETY

U.S. Consumer Product Safety Commission
Washington, D.C. 20207-0001
Phone: (301) 504-6816; Fax: (301) 504-0124 or 504-0025 Email: info@cpsc.gov
CPSC.gov

CPSC.gov/cpscpub/prerel/category/child.html
Information on baby product recalls – great for checking on second hand equipment.

KidSource.com/CPSC/safety_tips.html
Safety tips on making your baby products safe.

KidsHealth.org/parent/firstaid_safe/home/products.html
Find advice on choosing safe products.

PET SAFETY

Doggonesafe.com
Great educational site and tips on dog safety.

Cats.about.com/cs/catmanagement101/a/newbabyandcat.htm
Tips on safely integrating cats and babies.

POSTPARTUM DEPRESSION

National Women's Health Information Center
Department of Health and Human Services
4Woman.gov/faq/postpartum.htm
Information and links on postpartum depression.

Postpartum Dads
PostpartumDads.org
Support and information for fathers whose partners are suffering from postpartum depression or "baby blues".

Psycom.net/depression.central.post-partum.html
Heavily oriented towards treatment with drugs, information on postpartum depression and depression in general.

Postpartum Support International
PSI Postpartum Depression Helpline: 1.800.944.4PPD
Postpartum.net
Articles and links to other resources.

STAY-AT-HOME-DAD

AtHomeDad.com
Links to local groups, resources and articles.

Fatherhood.about.com/cs/stayhomedads
Articles and information on stay-at-home and work-at-home dads.

DadStaysHome.com
Active forum for stay-at-home dads.

TOBACCO CESSATION

Tobacco.org/Resources/tobsites.html
Quitting resources and anti-tobacco activism.

Mayo.edu/staff/ndc/FAQ.html
Mayo Clinic site includes articles, research and tips on quitting smoking.

QuitSmoking.about.com/od/preparetoquit/a/quitsmkingtools.htm
Cessation support website with articles and links.

WORK FAMILY BALANCE/TIME MANAGEMENT

MyGoals.com
Award-winning website helps with setting goals of all kinds – from financial to health to organization and relationship issues.

Blog.WashingtonPost.com/onbalance/
A Washington Post blog on balancing work and life with a specific section of archived articles for dads.

7 Family

LEARNING MORE/GETTING HELP

Whatever problems you may experience as a new father, always remember you are not alone, and as a result, there are resources available to you and your new family. To help you learn more about your circumstances, and if necessary, to get help, we have compiled the online *New Father Resource Center* on DadsAdventure.com. Check it out for updates and additions, or to recommend new resources that may help other fathers. Below is a representation of organizations and web sites from the online resource center that address issues encountered by dads and offer information to help you and your partner.

BABY CARE

BabyCenter.com
Offers useful tools for tracking your baby's growth and a highly involved community of moms who are always happy to share advice.

Baby.com
Illustrates where Johnson & Johnson products fit in your baby's life and includes articles on issues your baby may encounter.

American Academy of Pediatrics
AAP.org
Has baby care and health related information from a variety of sources including the Mayo Clinic and The American Academy of Pediatrics.
www.nlm.nih.gov/medlineplus/infantandnewborncare.html

BREASTFEEDING

La Leche League International (LLLI)
1400 N. Meacham Rd, Schaumburg, IL 60173
Phone: (847) 519-7730
LaLecheLeague.org
Get breastfeeding help, learn about breastfeeding and the law, find resources for health care providers and more.

BabyCenter.com/302_breastfeeding_1511828.bc
BabyCenter's breastfeeding section where you can find articles on every issue imaginable with comments by community members.

Breastmilk.com
Breastfeeding supplies and links to other resources.

CHILD ABUSE

National Child Abuse Hotline
1-800-4-A-CHILD
For parents seeking help with feelings of frustration and violence.
ChildHelpUSA.org

National Institute for Neurological Disorders and Stroke
Shaken Baby Information Page
NINDS.nih.gov/disorders/shakenbaby/shakenbaby.htm
Links to resources and information on abusive behavior, signs of infant abuse.

COLIC/EXCESSIVE CRYING

Colicnet.com
Colic Net is a collection of website links for information on Colic.

Colichelp.com
Good resource for tips on helping a baby experiencing colic. Includes stories from parents who have dealt with colic.

CONFLICT/ANGER MANAGEMENT

Conflict Center
Email: info@conflict-center.org
ConflictCenter.org

Relationships911.org
Information about conflict in a variety of different relationship scenarios. A resource for articles and books on the subject.

DAD Types

Singleparents.about.com/od/singledads
Advice and articles about single fathering.

Gay.com/families
Articles for gay fathers.

DAY CARE

NACCRRA-Child Care Resource and Referral
1319 F. Street, NW, Suite 500, Washington, DC 20004-1106
Phone: (202) 393-5501; Fax: (202) 393-1109
NACCRRA.net

ChildcareAware.org
Organization dedicated to providing helpful resources on childcare.

Babysitters.com
Childcare referral company focused on helping parents find local childcare that matches best with the needs of their children. Includes extensive directory of childcare providers, articles and resources.

DRUG AND ALCOHOL ASSISTANCE

Alcoholics Anonymous
Grand Central Station, P.O. Box 459, New York, N.Y. 10163
Alcoholics-Anonymous.org

National Organization on Fetal Alcohol Syndrome
NOFAS.org
Dedicated to eliminating birth defects caused by alcohol consumption during pregnancy and improving the life of those affected individuals and families.

Drug-abuse-treatment.org/resources.htm
Information on different types of treatment for drug abuse and where to find help near you.

GRIEF/LOSS

Grief Recovery Online for All Bereaved (GROWW)
GROWW.org/resource.htm
Many great links to organizations and online resources to help deal with the loss of an infant and recovering from grief in general.

Center for Loss in Multiple Birth, Inc. (CLIMB)
CLIMB-support.org
Organization that provides parent-to-parent support for those who have experienced the death of one or more multiple birth children.

IVF.com/misc.html
Article with information dealing with the loss of a baby.

CREATING TRADITIONS & MEMORIES

Want Do You Want To Remember Doing When Your Children Were Young?
What Do You Want Them To Remember?

The best memories often come from the traditions and rituals that you develop as a family. Parents can strengthen the family by creating memories through activities like planning camping trips with dad and making a tradition out of how you celebrate birthdays and holidays, bedtime routines, religious activities, and dinnertime. Merely repeating an activity every year makes it special and makes it a part of family lore.

Your children will come to expect the event which will help guarantee it keeps happening and over time becomes a shared memory. These fond memories give your child a sense of security, stability, and belonging along with pride in his family.

Indian Stories

If there ever was anything I ever did right as a dad, it was telling my children stories. I had never told one in my life before, but when I had a one and four year old, I found inspiration in a long ago Native American ancestor. Our stories evolved around an Indian family that just happened to be like ours (they added two more children as well), and those kids did cool and amazing things. Like caring for a baby eagle and returning him to his nest, taming horses and inventing irrigation. We were even involved with warring tribes, but always were the peace makers. Of course dad was a cool and amazing Chief, brave and strong with a great bod and a tribe that happily followed his lead. (Hey, they were my stories).

Never Too Soon

Starting a tradition with a baby may seem a little premature, but since the tradition's longevity makes it stronger, it's never too early to start.

- Create your own rituals from scratch. Some you'll borrow from your past but you can also get creative.
- Although your baby seems unaware right now, he's absorbing every sight and sound around him. For instance, he will be captivated by the bright colors, sparkling lights, and music of the holiday season or Fourth of July.
- Watch past holiday celebrations on video.
- Name It: Give your special tradition a catchy name making it fun and memorable. Sunday mornings while mom sleeps in can become the "fun day club" with dad.
- A tradition of spontaneity: Create some amazing memories on a whim. Instead of heading home after the game, hit the road and take an overnight trip to an amusement park or historical monument.
- Create personal traditions between dad and child.
- Repeat the personal tradition with each child as they reach a particular age or milestone. For example, when each child reaches age 14 take them on a special trip.

Memorable Ideas

- Sing your favorite songs together.
- Read stories or books aloud together.
- Snuggle together in mom and dad's bed on Saturday mornings.
- Give out nicknames (the little things count).
- Produce a family talent show.
- Saturdays can be dad's day to make breakfast with the kids.
- Pitch a tent and rough it with the kids.
- Share interests such as gardening, woodworking, singing, baking, hiking, or playing an instrument.
- Set aside one night a week to sit around the table and play board games.
- Share the value of being generous.
- Attend church services on Sunday.
- Drive out to the country to pick a pumpkin.
- Take an annual trip to cut the Christmas tree.
- Hang the stockings by the chimney with care.
- Have a one-on-one with your child every night before she goes to bed (especially parents who take frequent business trips).
- Make bath time an event with a special song or game.
- Participate in bedtime rituals such as telling or reading a story, singing a song, or saying a prayer.
- Get the extended family together for Sunday dinner on a weekly—or monthly—basis with grandparents, aunts, uncles, and cousins.
- Discover the traditions of your ancestors by exploring your racial or cultural history.
- Tell family stories (true stories and legends).
- Prepare traditional foods that honor your family's heritage.
- Take a family photo in the same spot every year.

My previously busy working life schedule was not really all that important. Time with my daughter was.

- Veteran Dad

RECORDING YOUR NEW FAMILY

TIPS FOR TAKING PICTURES OR FILMING THE BIRTH

1. Check with your hospital on rules regarding photography or video.
2. If you make the decision to appoint someone other than yourself to be the photographer, go with him or her to the hospital and ask to take a tour of the birthing area. It's also a good idea to watch a film of an actual birth in advance.
3. Make a decision, along with your partner, about how intimate you want the filming to be. Consider black and white photos if you decide to capture the moment without the graphic elements.
4. Capture the details; facial expressions, dad and mom working together, mom as she rests between contractions, etc.
5. Avoid using a flash or bright light. It can distract and annoy mom (and the hospital staff). Don't use a flash to shoot the baby as he's being born – it might hurt his eyes.
6. The photographer needs to understand that there are more important priorities during labor and birth.
7. When the baby arrives, capture her face. Ask the attending nurse where to stand for the best view.
8. Make sure you have a picture of yourself with your baby for the first time.

☐ **Document Her Development:** Take a series of pictures once a week that represent your baby's growth and developmental stages. By using the same location each time, the pictures will evolve into a story without words.

☐ **Unplanned (Candid) Shots are Best:** Just try to get him doing his thing.

☐ **Use Natural, Soft Light:** With natural light, your baby's face will glow; camera flashes and indoor lamps can make your baby's skin appear mottled. Using natural light is best, and most cameras will tell you when you don't have enough light to take a good shot. Try opening the drapes or window shades or moving to an area with more light.

☐ **Take Lots of Pictures from Different Angles:** Shoot your baby from above as she's looking up at you. Most people never think of taking photos of the backs of their babies, but these can be great shots and an interesting way to capture body language.

☐ **Baby's-Eye View:** Don't be afraid to get down and dirty when taking baby pictures. Photos taken on their level are charming, to say the least.

☐ **Try Black and White:** Black and white pictures accentuate the details of your baby's face and body, plus it gives them a nostalgic and classic feel.

Digital Pictures

For a good tutorial on digital photography go to vividlight.com/articles/3116.htm. Online photo sharing websites such as Shutterfly, Snapfish, KodakGallery, etc., are very popular. They allow you to upload your images, create albums and notify people by email to take a look at your pictures – all at no charge. You can also take digital pictures to photo outlets, as many have automated CD-ROM creators. Set up a system to sort and identify your best pictures or you will end up with a morass of picture files that will be cumbersome to access.

Getting Good Video

Be selective about what you are shooting. Think about what you plan to shoot and how you can best capture it before flipping on the "record" switch. After you get what you want, pause the tape and wait for your next opportunity. Avoid jerky movements and pause the recording when going from one person to another. Try not to stay on one thing for too long, and focus on details.

The Hospital Photo

These professional shots will capture each ruddy and squishy detail of your brand new baby. Refrain from buying the grand package. Just buy the 8X10, scan it at home and distribute it yourself.

Announce it

You can upload your photo to a drugstore website like Walmart.com or Target.com and choose a baby announcement style. You can pick them up at the store and send them yourself; or use a photo sharing website to create an announcement, have it shipped to you and then send it out or you can just print the photo and slip it into a baby announcement card from a stationery store.

I was taking so many pictures that if I didn't keep them organized, they turned into a big mess.

- Veteran Dad

7 Family

FAMILY FINANCE & ADMINISTRATION

When Money Is Tight

- Buy baby furniture second-hand, or borrow it from friends or family. There are a great number of stores that recycle baby items – lots of it is brand new – castoffs from baby showers or duplicate gifts. Just make sure they're compliant with today's standards for infant safety, and that they haven't been recalled.

- Mail out baby announcements to friends and relatives. Many will want to send gifts, gift certificates or money. Make sure you have registered at a baby store or big department store so people will be able to get you what you want and need.

- Register with online sites, such as babycenter.com and you'll not only get good information, you'll also get coupons and discounts on baby stuff.

Preparing For The Unthinkable

As new parents, you will have the very heavy responsibility of making arrangements in case something happens and you are not there to care for your child. While doing this ahead of time is prudent, mom will be very sensitive to the notion of leaving her baby without a mother, so use your discretion. Major tasks include:

- Make out a will (each parent needs one) or arrange a living trust. If you have access to legal assistance, take advantage. If not, economical on-line resources are available at legalzoom.com, nolo.com, legalconnection.com or findlaw.org.

- Specify who will care for your child if you are both unable to do so. This may take some time to work out if an obvious choice is not available. Write it down and make sure that person knows they have been chosen and agrees to do it.

- Consider purchasing life insurance on the breadwinner(s) to assure basic financial support for your family. Term insurance, which pays off in the event of your death, is the least expensive. Check out efinancial.com or moneycentral.msn.com for the best rates.

Get An Early Start On His College Education

Typically the final gift you will want to give your child before you send him off into the world is financial support for college. It can be expensive, but "529" plans, administered in 48 states, help by providing investment opportunities to parents and grandparents with state and federal tax-deferred growth and tax-free withdrawals for qualified higher education expenses. Each state determines its plan's structure. There can also be a state tax deduction, a matching grant, scholarships, protection from creditors and exemption from state financial aid calculations. There can also be plans that allow for the pre-purchase of tuition at colleges based on today's tuition rates. For more information, visit collegesavings.org.

Get Organized

With a baby on the way, it's a good idea to put together a well organized system for filing important documents. One way to do it is to create a hanging file for each broad category and fill it with manila folders for more specific topics. With the system in place, you'll have quick access to whatever you need, whenever you need it. Examples of typical family files:

- ☐ Birth Certificates
- ☐ Social Security Numbers
- ☐ Medical Records & Expenses
- ☐ House & Car Expenses
- ☐ Credit Cards
- ☐ Mortgage or Rental Contracts
- ☐ Insurance Papers
- ☐ Taxes
- ☐ Wills or Family Trust Documents

Make sure to carefully label every file. Better yet, buy a family/home organizing system that comes in a notebook or file box with pre-printed files for important contacts, wills, bank documents, etc.

 My wife and I just bought a new house and there's no way we can afford to keep it on one income. Yeah it was hard to leave Jessica with a stranger, but we got over it.

- Veteran Dad

PREPARING FOR YOUR FAMILY'S FUTURE

From the moment you know your new baby is on the way, chances are you'll spend time worrying about how to make ends meet. This section will help you get a handle on the important issues you face:

GET A HANDLE ON YOUR FINANCES

- **Get on the same page:** First, sit down with your partner and discuss the realities of your family's finances and what you are thinking about regarding new costs, income changes, lifestyle changes, etc.
- **Put a simple budget together:** Sort through your family's income and expenses. When you first run the numbers, if costs outweigh revenue, consider it normal.
- **Estimate increased expenses:** Such as diapers, day care costs, an increase in health insurance premiums, any life/disability insurance you want to add.

DECIDE ON ONE OR TWO INCOMES

About half of new moms return to work within a few months after birth. You and/or your partner may want her to quit her job and stay home with the baby. Perhaps it makes more sense for you to stay home. Perhaps she (or you) could work part time with the baby in day care a few days a week, or one of you could work out of the house. Think through available alternatives, and consider the costs of employment including taxes, day care, commuting costs, etc.

Seeing exactly by how much, and for how long, you expect your cumulative income to drop will indicate how much you need to cut back or have in savings to tide you over.

MAJOR CHANGES MAY BE APPROPRIATE

If you have a big mortgage that is dependent upon two incomes, you may want to reconsider being house rich even with a baby on the way. If you have a long commute that adds hours away from home on top of a long workday, you might want to look at employment or housing alternatives. Moving or changing jobs is increasingly common during the ramp up to "D-day", and major lifestyle changes involving how and where you want to raise a family are increasingly common.

HEALTH INSURANCE TO DO'S

Contact your insurance provider and ask how much you'll need to pay out of pocket (called your "co-payment") and if you face any restrictions on your choice of health-care facilities. Also, arrange to have your newborn added; this is usually required within 30 days and it is up to you to get it handled.

IF SHE DOES NOT HAVE INSURANCE

About 13% of women who become pregnant each year do not have health insurance. If your partner is not insured, it is important that you check out alternatives and resources early so that she receives appropriate prenatal care. The cost of delivery alone is $6,000 – $8,000 for a normal pregnancy and higher with a high risk pregnancy. Obtaining private health insurance after she becomes pregnant will be almost impossible because it will be considered a pre-existing condition. Suggestions:

- Check out Medicaid, a federally funded program for low income persons. They will accept women who are already pregnant.
- Contact an obstetrician's or hospital's patient accounts department and ask about their policies and your alternatives. They can refer you to resources in your region, including Medicaid.
- Healthcare discount plans may be helpful (try americanpregnancy.org or ameriplan.org). First, ask your health care provider what discount you would receive if you paid cash. Ask about setting up a payment plan or if they offer a sliding scale.
- If you are having an uncomplicated pregnancy, consider giving birth at a birthing center. Typically, the cost will be much lower. Many birth centers also provide sliding scales, payment plans and accept Medicaid. Despite planning on an uncomplicated pregnancy, you should check what their procedures are if an emergency does arise.
- Ask about insurance coverage for your baby as well. The State Children's Health Insurance Program (CHIP) is designed to help children in working families with incomes too high to qualify for Medicaid.

 I liked living near the beach, but we moved to Riverside to reduce my commute as well as our mortgage payment so Mary doesn't have to go back to work for a while.

- Veteran Dad

7 Family

Notes

Notes

DEALING WITH HER SYMPTOMS

How to Tell If He's Not Well

Babies give signals when they aren't feeling well. The most obvious are fever, runny nose, cough or rash. There are also less obvious signals: seems lethargic or very cranky, not interested in anything or anyone around him, has little or no appetite, spitting up more than usual, or stools are either very hard or runny. The intensity and duration of such symptoms are also factors that will help you, a nurse or a doctor determine how to treat them.

Fevers and Colds

Fever is how a baby responds to an infection. If his temperature is over 101 degrees, he has a fever. If he's less than two months old and his temperature is higher than 100 degrees, if a low grade fever has lasted longer than a few days, or if there is a rash along with the fever call your pediatrician.

Sniffles and respiratory congestion can make your baby miserable. Make sure her airway is clear and that she is not having difficulty breathing. Call the doctor if your baby's cough comes from deep in her chest, if her breathing is labored, or if she is wheezing.

Falls and Bumps On the Head

No matter how careful you are your baby will fall. If he tumbles off a couch, falls out of his high chair or slips out of your arms after a bath, you should do a thorough check for injuries and watch him closely for a while afterwards. If he cries after he falls, it's a good sign that he's not seriously injured. If he has fallen on his head or back, be even more careful in your observations. Watch him carefully for 24 hours. Take him to the doctor or emergency room if he:

Warning!

Don't give your baby any medicine without first checking with your pediatrician. A small dose of an adult pain reliever or decongestant may seem reasonable, but a baby's nervous and immune systems are very different from yours and present special issues that you are unlikely to be aware of.

- Seems weak or confused.
- Is having trouble moving any part of his body or there seems to be a deformity of an arm or leg.
- There is blood in the whites of his eyes or pink fluid coming out of his nose or ears.
- Shows signs of a concussion, such as crossed eyes or pupils that are unequal in size, or if he vomits.
- If he cries loudly when you move any part of his body.
- If he is sleeping more than normal.

Raising a Road Warrior

While you want to be careful in the first 6 weeks when their immune systems are just cranking up, there is no reason to keep a healthy baby at home. Make sure the diaper bag is fully stocked for an outing that will last more than several hours; if all day, add a daypack with extra diapers, undershirts, footed pajamas, an extra blanket, bottles and a few of his favorite toys. Include a plastic bag for disposing of diapers.

If the temperature is over 75°, a diaper and t-shirt underneath a pair of footed pajamas is usually good enough. If it's breezy, add a light jacket and a hat to keep the sun off his face and his head warm. Add layers as the temperature gets lower.

 I guess the most surprising thing was that none of the 200 terrible things I thought may happen did happen.

- Veteran Dad

PREPARING FOR WHEN HE IS SICK

When to Call The Doctor

Whether it's coughing, diarrhea, crossed eyes, not eating, or anything else, if you think your baby is ill for any reason then check with a nurse hot line or your pediatrician. When it comes to your baby's health, err on the side of calling the doctor too often, as you may not be able to tell the big problems from little ones. Just call the doctor (that's what the doctors tell us). He will let you know if you are calling too much. It's also essential to get to know your baby's doctor by going to his well-baby checks. Go with mom or take turns with her.

Become the Family Paramedic

As Chief Roughhousing Officer and with many adventures with your child ahead, you should consider adding the role of family paramedic to assure a competent response to your child's health issues. Basic resources and requirements include:

- **Emergency Phone Numbers** – Keep number readily available (next to the phone) for: doctor, nurse hot line, the local emergency room, regional poison center, trustworthy neighbor, etc.

- **Nurse Hot Line -** Experienced pediatric nurses are readily available 24 hours a day by phone and will spend all the time you need talking about any issue related to your baby's health. They will also tell you if you need to contact your doctor. Find out which hot line your doctor recommends, and call for even minor reasons to get to know them.

- **Medical Guide** – Purchase the latest edition of a comprehensive guide from a reputable source such as the *American Academy of Pediatrics Guide to Your Child's Symptoms*, the *American Medical Association Family Medical Guide*, or the *Mayo Clinic Family Health Book*.

- **First Aid Kit & Guide -** When you need a bandage, antiseptic, or cream for a minor burn, you need it readily available, so keep a well stocked kit handy. Keep a concise first aid guide in your kit and take it with you on hikes and outings.

- **A First Aid Class -** Ensures your family will have a dad who knows what he's doing in an emergency. Information on classes and handling emergencies can be found at RedCross.org.

The Dreaded Nose Bulb

A baby cannot blow his nose, so you will need to do it for him using a nose bulb (looks like a small turkey baster). He will hate having it stuck up his nose and will thrash around, making it a very difficult maneuver. To get the job done, lie him face-up on the bed, wrap your arm around his head and place your hand on his chest to keep him from moving. With your other hand squeeze the air out of the bulb, quickly place it gently but snuggly in one nostril, and let the bulb expand. Repeat in other nostril. Being quick is the key.

How To Prevent SIDS

While still a common fear, the incidence of SIDS has dropped in half due to the American Academy of Pediatric's Back to Sleep campaign, which recommends that you:
- Put your baby to sleep on her back with no toys, loose blankets, pillows, quilts, or other soft materials. This goes for nighttime, daytime naps, as well as naps at grandma's house.
- Do not allow smoking around your baby by anyone.
- Dress your baby in light sleep clothing so he does not overheat and keep the room at a comfortable temperature.
- Minimize that flat spots on your baby's head by changing the direction that your baby lies in the crib.
- Consider buying a sleep sack, especially in colder climates.

Most SIDS deaths occur at 2 to 4 months; after 6 months, no worries.

6 Safe & Healthy

" *If you don't have a first aid kit, you should get one.*

- Veteran Dad **"**

CHILD CARE SELECTION GUIDELINES

As more women decide to continue with a career after childbirth, and even more families are faced with the reality that two incomes are a necessity, childcare has become a reality for many families. As a new father you may not be aware that you have some options when it comes to choosing child-care, and more importantly, you also have the responsibility of finding a safe and reliable provider.

Various Options

There are four basic options of child-care:

- **Formal child-care center:** Part of a chain or a non-profit. Typically large and take children from as young as 6 weeks up until school age. Required to be licensed and have state mandated staffing ratios.
- **Family day-care home:** Run directly out of a child-care provider's home. Will take much fewer children than a center, but may not require a license to be run. Usually less expensive than a center.
- **In-home care:** Live-in nanny or au pair. Most expensive option but provides child-care within arms reach.
- **Family or friends:** Less structured arrangement (usually). May be cheapest option, however, especially if grandparents are the caregivers.

Tips for Selecting a Provider

There are a few basic things to keep in mind when evaluating any caregiver.

- **Verify accreditation/licensing:** Child Care Aware (childcareaware.org) is a great resource to check on specific state's licensing requirements. You can also use your state's licensing bureau to check past complaints about a specific provider. Remember that some states don't require home-based providers to be accredited, so be extra thorough when researching these types of providers and do background checks and contact more than one previous employer.
- **Check references:** But also take the time to speak with parents picking up/ dropping off kids outside the facility.
- **Tour the center:** Tours should be encouraged and staff should be open and attentive to any questions you have. Make at least one unscheduled visit, in addition to the initial scheduled tour. Any provider that isn't completely open with information or has a problem with your thoroughness should be absolutely avoided.
- **Check the space:** Ensuring that the facility is child-proof should go without saying, but your child's safety should always be a top priority so a comprehensive look over the child-care center is essential.

Family Care

While often cost effective, family care can have its own drawbacks. Never hesitate to remove your child from an environment where your wishes as a parent aren't being kept (not laying your infant on her back for naps, for example). This can be difficult if it's grandma whose caring for the child, but your child's health and safety are more important than bruised egos.

Trust your instincts.

If you're unsure about a provider during the interview process, go with your intuition and steer clear. Even if you can't say what bothers you, it's better to trust your instincts and find someone you do trust.

- **Observe the employees:** For toddlers, the child to caregiver ratio should never be more than 4-1 (under 12 months should be 3-1). Observe director and employee interaction and inquire about employee turnover rates; the lower the better. Verify employees are CPR certified, and ask to see current certifications.
- **Verify drop-in and pick-up policies:** Be wary about places that limit times when parents can stop by (one exception might be prescribed nap times, though). You should have access to your child whenever you want. Confirm the center will only release a child to a parent or authorized family member.

Final Thoughts

There is conflicting research about the effects of child-care. In a good environment, child-care can contribute to intellectual and social development, and yet children who spend more time in child-care have slightly more potential for behavior and learning issues. Since most of us don't have many options when it comes to childcare just do your best to find the right place for your child. Once placed, though, remember to keep your guard up. While most children respond well to a strong, nurturing care environment you still want to be on the lookout for extended behavioral and developmental inconsistencies that crop up after the child is in a care setting.

My wife and I decided on a live-in. After interviewing several people we finally chose one. But after two weeks I didn't feel right about this person. So, we got rid of her and went through the interviewing process again. The one we hired the second time around is still with us.

- Veteran Dad

6 Safe & Healthy

INTRODUCING PETS TO YOUR BABY

DOGS

Introducing your new baby to your dog is almost like bringing a baby home to a sibling; if handled incorrectly it can cause rivalry and hurt feelings. By taking a few simple precautions, though, your dog and baby should eventually become the best of friends.

- If you're going to take your dog to an obedience class, do it before the baby arrives, since you won't have the time after baby comes home. If your dog doesn't know basic commands then you might want to seriously consider classes.
- Any changes to the house rules need to be made before the baby arrives. You don't want your dog to associate the baby with her prohibition from sleeping in your bed.
- Have a vet check for parasites or other health concerns four to five months before the baby is born.
- Introduce your dog to baby blankets, lotions, rattles and toys before the baby comes home.
- To get your dog used to the baby's scent you can send home a blanket or gown from the hospital that the baby has been wrapped in.
- Have someone other than mom carry the baby inside the house for the first time. This will allow mom to greet the dog and may cut down on jealousy the dog feels later on over mom's attention to the baby.
- Try not to scold the dog while holding the baby, so that the dog doesn't connect the baby with discipline.
- Use positive reinforcement as much as possible (a treat or a hug), and reassure the dog whenever the baby cries.
- Make sure you still spend one-on-one time with your dog (during baby naps, or on walks).
- It might be a while until your dog is fully relaxed around the baby, so just be patient.

Tips and Warnings

- ☐ Make sure your dog heeds a 'Quiet!' or 'Hush!' command. She can still guard the house, but can be quieted when the baby is asleep.
- ☐ Get a reign on jumping up before the baby comes home, and make sure her nails are trimmed.
- ☐ Never leave your dog alone with the baby. Even the best-behaved dog can become frustrated with a baby's cries and will act instinctively.

Breeds of Concern: Sexually intact male dogs and dogs trained or bred to be aggressive are not safe around children. Pit bulls, chows and rottweilers often fit this description. As a parent, it is now your responsibility to be honest about how your dog has been raised and whether it is safe around your child.

Do What You Need to Do: If the dog shows aggression, or if you don't fully trust him, remember your priority is to protect your baby and the dog must go. Choosing between a new baby you barely know, and a dog that has been with you for years may be difficult, but think it through and do what you need to.

CATS

Scratches are a danger and cats are capable of jumping to get to an infant. Many cats find curling up and sleeping on a warm baby inviting, but this poses a risk of suffocation for the baby so extra vigilance is in order.

EXOTICS

If you own a large carnivorous reptile you probably don't need reminding that they can be dangerous. Anything that considers your infant a potential snack should either be removed from the home or monitored with extreme care.

Additional resources on the web:

Ehow.com/how_4579_introduce-new-baby.html
Petco.com/caresheets/dog/Dog_New_Baby.pdf

- Smaller reptiles and amphibians can harbor dangerous bacterial diseases. Always wash thoroughly after handling them and before touching anything else.
- Birds may harbor parasites, and many people are allergic to feathers. Birds that are allowed to roam freely about the home pose obvious risks.

 I looked up and there was my dog coming down the stairs carrying the baby by its head.

- Veteran Dad

6 Safe & Healthy

INFANT CPR & CHOKING BASICS

Learn CPR

Mickey Eisenberg, M.D.'s LearnCPR.org offers basic infant CPR and choking instructions in 30-40 second videos and the simple directions on this card (both available in 7 languages). You can easily download the videos to your computer to review with the instructions below and keep readily accessible. Learn CPR stresses that this cannot replace real CPR or first aid training and recommends attending a course in your community offered by the American Heart Association (call 1-800 AHA USA1), the American Red Cross and many local fire departments.

First Aid for Choking Infants

1. Determine if your infant can cry or cough. If not, proceed to next step.

2. Give 5 back blows

3. Give 5 chest thrusts

4. Repeat steps 2 & 3

Repeat above until effective or the infant becomes unconscious. If the infant becomes unresponsive, perform CPR- if you see an object in the throat or mouth, remove it.

CPR for Infants Who Are Not Breathing

1. Shout and Tap

Shout and gently tap the child on the shoulder. If there is no response, position the infant on his or her back

2. Open The Airway

Open the airway using a head tilt lifting of chin. Do not tilt the head too far back.

3. Give 2 Gentle Breaths

If the baby is NOT breathing give 2 small gentle breaths. Cover the baby's mouth and nose with your mouth. Each breath should be 1 second long. You should see the baby's chest rise with each breath.

4. Give 30 Compressions

Give 30 gentle chest compressions at the rate of 100 per minute. Use two or three fingers in the center of the chest just below the nipples. Press down approximately one-third the depth of the chest.

5. Repeat

Repeat with 2 breath and 30 compressions. After two minutes of repeated cycles call 911 and continue giving breaths and compressions.

EMERGENCY MEDICAL INSTRUCTIONS FOR BABIES

When to Call 911

- ☐ Your child is not breathing or has difficulty such as breathing very rapidly
- ☐ He or she is unconscious
- ☐ Has been injured in or by a moving vehicle
- ☐ Serious wound or fractured bone
- ☐ Serious bleeding or severe burns
- ☐ Experiencing a seizure
- ☐ Choking on something you cannot help him expel (see choking)
- ☐ A deformity of the skull, possible skull fracture
- ☐ Bleeding or clear fluid from the nose, ear, or mouth
- ☐ Has fallen more than 5 feet onto a hard surface
- ☐ Experiencing a condition you feel is life or limb threatening

Call 911 or yell for someone else to do so. Push the speakerphone button on your phone so you can hear instructions while you treat your child.

When to Go to the ER

- ☐ Evaluate a head injury
- ☐ X-Ray a possible broken bone
- ☐ A cut that may need stitches
- ☐ High fever or other serious illness
- ☐ Another condition that you feel may need emergent care

You can also call your doctor or nurse hotline for advice; they may save you a costly emergency room visit.

Keep First Aid Kit Handy

Keep a first aid kit handy that includes the following items for a baby:

- ☐ Assemble a first aid kit for your home and one for each car
- ☐ Nonstick sterile pads for stopping bleeding
- ☐ Adhesive bandages of different sizes
- ☐ Liquid soap/sanitizer (clean minor cuts and scrapes)
- ☐ Eye wash solution to flush eyes
- ☐ Thermometer to diagnose fevers
- ☐ Pain and fever reducers with dosages for an infant or baby
- ☐ Antibiotic ointment (prevents infection)
- ☐ Burn ointment to sooth and protect skin
- ☐ Syrup of Ipecac (if use advised by Poison Control Center)
- ☐ Gauze bandage roll and adhesive tape
- ☐ Small "ace" bandage
- ☐ A guidebook on first aid for children

If Going To Great Outdoors Add

- ☐ SPF 15+ sunscreen; use only on babies at least six months old
- ☐ Knife with tweezers for removing splinters, ticks
- ☐ Hydrocortisone cream for insect bites, rashes, minor burns
- ☐ Insect repellent for babies
- ☐ Cold pack to reduce swelling from bumps, bites, etc.
- ☐ Snake bite kit (just kidding, mom, it's for dad.)
- ☐ Cell phone

Head Injuries Require Extra Vigilance

Head bonks are common among babies due to the high proportion of their body weight in their heads. Falls are the main cause, so be watchful and protective as a general rule and avoid tossing your child in the air. If he does hurt his head, you will need to determine how serious it is and how to respond. The scalp is rich with blood vessels, so even a minor cut there can bleed profusely. Even if he appears ok, he may an internal injury that can be very serious.

If it is obviously serious, call 911. If he won't stop crying, vomits multiple times, indicates unusual weakness or has pupils of unequal size or crossed eyes, take him to the ER. If no injury is evident but he fell from a significant height or was hit with significant force, call his doctor or nurse line for advice and direction; he may have suffered a concussion.

Poison Control Center - 800 222-1222

Call 800-222-1222 if you suspect your baby has ingested a toxic substance. Call before symptoms develop and even if you just have a question about poisons. They will ask what was ingested (see the label), an estimate of how much, and when it happened. The Center will tell you what to do.

6 Safe & Healthy

WHEN TO BABY PROOF: Stay Ahead of the Curve

Age	Height	What can he do?	What to look For	Room	Actions to take
3 Months	Arms length up from the ground, or anywhere he can reach	Grabbing – anything within reach of his grubby little hands will get picked up and go into his mouth	Cords/curtains, sharp or small objects, anything that can be pulled	Living Room	Remove all small objects (change, pens, hair clips, etc.) Wrap up curtains and cords Remove plants or put out of reach
				Kitchen	Ensure knives are secured Wrap up curtains and cords
				Bedroom/baby room	Wrap up curtains and cords (pay attention to any near baby's crib) Keep fluffy blankets, pillows, or stuffed animals out of crib
				Bathroom	Keep baby out of arms reach of (nearly) everything
6 Months	May be sitting up – 1 1/2 feet off the ground	Mobility – by scooting or rolling he can now get to even more dangerous stuff	Electrical outlets and plugs, anything that can be pulled down	Living Room	Secure fireplace screen and tools Cover exposed outlets and secure exposed cords Ensure lamps, TV, etc. can't be pulled down by cords
				Kitchen	Keep high chair away from walls (strong kicks against wall can knock the chair over) Use plastic plates and dishes
				Bedroom/baby room	Remove mobiles or hanging toys from crib (by five months) Ensure crib is at least two feet from windows Cover outlets, secure cords
				Bathroom	Install toilet guard Put non-slip mat in tub Install cabinet locks Keep electric items (hair dryers, etc.) put away when not in use
9 Months	May be standing against furniture – 2 – 2 1/2 feet off the ground	Crawling – more prone to falling injuries as he is even more mobile and begins to experiment with walking	Stairs, table corners, drawers and cabinets, toilets	Living Room	Pad table corners and fireplace hearth Move furniture away from windows Put gates between rooms and at the top/bottom of stairs
				Kitchen	Install cabinet locks Install oven lock and stove knob covers Keep mouse and insect traps in inaccessible places
				Bedroom/baby room	Ensure toy chest lid stays up when opened Be aware of things that can be climbed on (rocking chair, open dresser drawers, etc.)
				Bathroom	Install knob covers on bath Put non-slip mat on outside of tub Always keep tub empty of water
One Year	Fully standing, on tip toes and fully reaching – over 3 feet off the ground	Walking and reaching – he's now a foot taller (then when he only crawled)	Everything	Living Room	Ensure nothing is low enough for him to reach and pull down Put decals (at his height) on sliding doors
				Kitchen	Use back burners when cooking Keep refrigerator magnets out of reach Lock dishwasher Keep pet dishes in separate, locked room
				Bedroom/baby room	Keep changing table items away from edge of table
				Bathroom	Consider keeping baby out with gate (at this age, there's just too much he can get into in there when not supervised)

KEEPING YOUR BABY SAFE

Nothing's worse than seeing your child hurt and knowing you could have prevented it. So after he arrives, keep your protective instincts alert and operational. To help them fully kick in, take a first aid class oriented toward children and buy a family first aid kit.

Dad Safety – The First Line of Defense

Basic male behavior can lean more toward the risk-taking macho variety than the assessing hazards and limiting risk type. Many men find, however, that once the baby is born (and even before), they begin to reevaluate hobbies (skydive much?) and habits (how fast do you drive?). Why? You are the only dad she has, and it's in her best interest that you stick around for a while.

Some Things to Keep in Mind

- **Smoking -** Unlike you, your baby can't move out of harm's way. When you smoke around him, he gets even more of a hit than you do.

- **Toxins –** Including paints, lacquers (even nail polish and remover), and insecticides. Do not use them indoors or in the vicinity of your baby. A newborn's immune system is not fully developed, and these substances can be harmful even in small doses.

- **Pockets –** Empty your pockets before handling your baby. Things can fall out of your pockets without you even noticing and even swallowing a single penny might require your baby to go through surgery.

- **Sun Protection –** Because your baby has sensitive skin, it's important to avoid using sunscreen until she's 6-months old. Use other methods of keeping her out of the sun, like a baby-seat canopy. If you're taking a stroller walk, and the sun is in her face, just hang a light blanket over the stroller's canopy to shield her.

- **Water and Bathing –** Children under 1 year old drown most commonly in bathtubs, buckets, and toilets. In fact, your baby can drown in as little as two inches of water. You should never stray more than an arm's length from your baby while she's bathing.

- **Salt and Honey –** There are several food items that you should definitely avoid. Although you cannot keep sodium out of the baby's food, excess salt is detrimental to her kidneys and blood pressure. And up until a baby turns one, you should NEVER feed honey to a baby. Honey can cause infant botulism, which could lead to death.

The Slide-and-Hide Technique
Used toilet-paper tubes make superb measuring devices. If an object can slide down the tube, it can also slide down your baby's breathing passage. Don't let your baby fall prey to asphyxiation or choking.

Baby Proofing – Things that Should be Done before the Baby Arrives

- Set the water heater to 120 degrees to avoid scalding the baby.
- Check smoke detectors and install in any rooms that need them.
- Get a fire extinguisher. If you already have one, make sure that it has recently been inspected.
- Cover radiators/space heaters.
- Bolt bookshelves and other free standing cabinets to walls.
- Post emergency phone numbers (pediatrician, poison control center, etc.) near the phone. Or program them into the phone's speed dial.

ADOPTING A "BABY'S-EYE" VIEW

Even after you've baby-proofed, you should be continually assessing the safety of your baby's environment. One way is to get down to his level and look around. Is the surface he's lying on secure? Are there small objects around him that could get into his mouth? Sharp objects he can grab? Try crawling around and see if your knees discover any "unwanted" items and you'll see what the baby might run into as well.

> *I used to smoke two packs a day. When my baby was born, I walked out of the hospital and threw the cigarettes away. Every time I wanted to smoke, I would pick my daughter up and look into her eyes.*
> *- Veteran Dad*

NEW DAD STATUS CHECK-UPS

Instructions: Jot down your thoughts and track your progress as you transform into a dad.

First Status Checkup Coinciding With 6 Week Baby Checkup

Most new dads hit bottom around 6 weeks, so this is a good time to take stock of your progress. The initial excitement, attention and help are gone, replaced by exhaustion, frustration and ambivalence about having a baby, a mate who is in worse shape, and an incessantly demanding infant who may be screaming regularly with colic. Your work suffers, your sex life is history, exercise and time for yourself are rare, and there is no end in sight to your new life of drudgery and servitude (when it is time to vent, you want to get it all out). Take comfort in that you're halfway through the 3-month hump, after which babies quit crying all the time and start sleeping longer.

Do Status Check Every Quarter For First Year

It is easy to lose perspective. Asking yourself some basic questions can help you get a grip on what is happening and clarify how you are doing as a father. There are no right or wrong answers; just questions:

Your Baby

- ☐ How do you feel about your baby?
- ☐ What were some of the best times you have had?
- ☐ What frustrates you about your child?
- ☐ Are you confident and capable in caring for your baby?
- ☐ How much time have you spent with your baby this week?
- ☐ What would you like to do better?

Your Mate

- ☐ Have your feelings about your wife changed?
- ☐ How about her feelings towards you?
- ☐ Are you working together as partners?
- ☐ Is the romance returning?
- ☐ How do you feel about her as a mom?
- ☐ What would you like to do better with her?

Yourself

- ☐ How are you feeling? Have you changed?
- ☐ What things do you like about being a father? What do you dislike?
- ☐ Are you satisfied with the job you are doing?
- ☐ Are you angry? Does your anger get in the way?
- ☐ Are you depressed? If so, are you getting it handled?
- ☐ What would you like to do better?

Date:	6 WEEKS										
Your Baby											
Your Mate											
Your Self											

1st Quarter

Date: _____

Your Baby

Your Mate

Your Self

2nd Quarter

Date: _____

Your Baby

Your Mate

Your Self

3rd Quarter

Date: _____

Your Baby

Your Mate

Your Self

4th Quarter

Date: _____

Your Baby

Your Mate

Your Self

Notes

Notes

5 Transforming

GET AHEAD OF THE CURVE!

The peak moments of fatherhood occur when you engage your child in adventures you enjoy together. They learn a great deal from these experiences, you learn how important you are to them, and the connection you build lasts a lifetime. Making a list of ideas means you will never have to try and think of something to do, so check pages 8C for ideas, brainstorm and add your own, and start checking them off. There is no better habit to develop as a dad.

Date	Adventures We Can Have Together	Done
	example: Front Pack Tour of Yard	☐
		☐
		☐
		☐
		☐
		☐
		☐
		☐
		☐
		☐
		☐
		☐
		☐
		☐
		☐
		☐
		☐
		☐
		☐

Date	What I Can Teach My Child	Done
	example: Roll Over	☐
		☐
		☐
		☐
		☐
		☐
		☐
		☐
		☐
		☐
		☐
		☐
		☐
		☐
		☐
		☐
		☐
		☐
		☐

A New Father's Transformation Milestones

	Milestones & Challenges	What To Shoot For	How Are You Doing?
Deploy	Ready or not, "I'm pregnant!" is the kickoff! (44% of us say not). To become part of your child's life, you need to get ready before his birth. This includes getting in sync with your mate, dealing with your concerns, thinking through what kind of dad you want to be, etc.	Deploy means get organized and get ready: • Go to the doctor visits and ask questions • Help her through pregnancy and talk to her • Feel your baby kick and talk to him as well • Get comfortable with basic baby care • Prepare yourself to be her childbirth coach	(Date:) _____
Deliver	When her labor kicks in, it is time to deliver. Coaching her through childbirth is intense and perhaps harrowing, but you will do it. Next, welcome your baby into the world! Then take your family home where you will need to seriously deliver for weeks on end.	Deliver means be ready and get it done: • Be her calm, reassuring birth coach • Make the birth special for mom and dad • Get hands-on in caring for your baby • Take care of mom; do whatever you can • Get sleep when you can; you will need it	
Deprived	With little sleep, a demanding baby and worn out mom, plan on hitting the wall when the adrenaline runs out after a few weeks. Even so, you still have to get up to care for your baby and then get up and go to work, with no end in sight through your bleary eyes.	Deprived is being exhausted and feeling the life you knew and loved is over: • Remember this phase will pass • Assess mom for baby blues (See page 4-F) • Assess yourself (take 6 week checkup) • Focus on the basics; let the rest slide	
Discover	Hey, you've gotten the hang of taking care of your baby! And after 3 months, her crying cuts way back! And she smiles when she sees you! She's still lots of work, but you learned what works and are getting a second wind and a sense of control over your life.	Discovery means enlightenment: • Teach your baby to play peek-a-boo • Take her out on your own once a week • Think about future adventures together • Start romancing the new mom in your life • Consider the kind of father you want to be	
Delight	Now this is getting fun! He gets all excited when you walk in the room and he can roll over, laugh, learn to do tricks. You have a new bud (or budette)! This is where bonding with your baby can skyrocket and lock you into a strong connection for life. Ride this wave!	Delight means fun and fulfillment for you: • Teach your baby to do 3 things (to start) • Share the fun with mom • Fanaticize about family adventures • Make your early experience as a new father positive to build momentum for the future	
Dad	A dad puts his child's needs before his own, protects her from all threats, looks forward to their future together and builds a new sense of pride, confidence and purpose. When tough, remember it is not just a learning curve, you are on a growth curve as a man.	Reflect on the kind of father you've become! Continue to do your best as a dad; the life-time payback is enormous. Make the most of it as a family – with mom- and you will find new moms love their baby's new daddy. Welcome to the brotherhood of fatherhood!	

MY GOALS AS A FATHER

What Kind of Father Do I Want To Be?

A great question to ask. Start by thinking of your own father or a man who served in this role, and then ask yourself some questions. Here are some to get you started:

✓ What did he do best as a father?
✓ What would you do differently?
✓ What did you learn from him that you want to pass on to your children?
✓ Are there other fathers (or friends) who you want to emulate?
✓ Do you feel good about becoming a father?
✓ What concerns do you have?
✓ What values and attributes do you want to pass on to your children?
✓ What are your strengths and weaknesses for being a father?
✓ What kind of relationship do you want with your child?
✓ What do you want to do together as he grows?
✓ How do you want to work together with your mate to raise your child?

You Are Changing The World

By doing your best as a dad, you will be on the front lines of a renaissance in fatherhood in America. You are improving the world for all children, including your own, by setting an example for the fathers who follow you.

Spell Out Your Goals and Commitments

Goals give us a path to follow and stating them is the first step toward meeting them. Take an initial shot at listing your goals as a father and periodically revisit and update them to stay on track. (This is for you, not the baby book.)

Date	My commitments to my child	Initials
	Suggestion: You can count on me no matter what	

Date	Values I want to teach my child	Initials

Date	How I want to be remembered as a father	Initials

My dad worked hard, but when he was home, he liked to be with me. I could always talk to him about stuff. I still can. I hope to raise my son the same way.

- Veteran Dad

HOW TO TRANSFORM INTO A DAD

This pull out provides tools to help you chart your course and a private, personal journal to track your progress. Any major challenge you take on in life – and no other can be more profound than fatherhood – warrants planning, preparing and improving as you go, and this will enable you to get it done. It will help you not just survive, but thrive as a dad by facilitating your preparation of a game plan that you can adjust as you gain experience and your child grows.

1. **Inventory Your Concerns as a Dad-To-Be**

   Review the list of common concerns of dads-to-be on page 5-B and check off or add those that pertain to you. Then note the three most important ones (the rest fall under a basic rule for new fathers: don't sweat the small stuff):

   _____

   _____

   _____

2. **Take Stock of Your Attributes as a Dad**

   Every man brings strengths and weaknesses to fatherhood, and an assessment of your "dad attributes" before your child arrives sure beats discovering your weaknesses the hard way down the road. Consider how you stack up on:

   - ✓ Patience
   - ✓ Building relationships
   - ✓ Collaboration (with mom)
   - ✓ Selflessness (i.e., not selfish)
   - ✓ Playfulness (i.e., never growing up)
   - ✓ Bad habits (tobacco, alcohol, drugs)
   - ✓ Income production
   - ✓ Time for your family
   - ✓ Courage & perseverance

   Consider your weaknesses and how you can overcome them. If you have a habit incompatible with being a dad, plan on dealing with it. Consider your strengths and how you can use them. If you have a good amount of time or flexibility to be with your child, what will you do with her? Taking note and strategizing early on will enable you to get a handle on any challenge and deal with it constructively.

3. **Set Some Goals**

   Most moms are physically, emotionally and socially driven to make sacrifices from the moment the indicator turns blue, and then are surrounded by mom mentors who show them the way. We dads are left to our own motivations and devices. Since we are on our own, defining our goals for our own fatherhood is essential; otherwise, we run the risk of getting caught up in the initial turbulence and letting circumstance chart our course. Use the tool on the following page (5-J) to think through your initial goals as a new father and then track how you do.

4. **Strategize On Re-Balancing Your Life**

   Research has found 75% of fathers want more time with their children. Start early on adjusting to the needs and your desires for your new family, especially if you have opportunities now that are unlikely to come along in the future. See *Work Balance Options* on page 5-F. Deal constructively with finances, income, career paths, one or two paychecks, etc. and if there are no short-term solutions, strategize and set goals for resolving them in the future.

5. **Track Your Transformation**

   You are in the midst of a personal transformation that will profoundly change you. The *New Father's Transformation Milestones* on page 5-K describes six stages through which all new fathers must pass to become a real dad. Check them out, add your own goals under "What to Shoot For," and note your progress over the first year.

6. **Conduct Periodic Status Checks**

   A status check on your progress as a father will boost your confidence and provide a basis for adjusting your goals and strategies. Start with one coinciding with your baby's 6-week check-up and then do one quarterly for the 1st year.

7. **Plan Your First Adventure With Your Kid**

   Actually, make a list of the adventures you want with your child and another on what you would like to teach her (start with the form on the flip side). This will set your sights beyond the drudgery to the nirvana of raising a child.

> *You get a lot of messages that women have maternal instincts and you kind of get the message that they're the only ones that do. But the fact is that dads have instincts too and I think that as long as you follow that I don't think you make too many bad choices.*
>
> *- Veteran Dad*

WHEN YOU GET OVERWHELMED OR CLOSE TO IT

If you find the whole scene seriously getting to you, do something about it:

- **Try to get enough sleep.** Grab a nap when possible – a little sleep can go a long way.
- **Be realistic.** The demands of fatherhood can easily push you past your limits, and you can't do everything. Let yourself off the hook once in a while and de-stress.
- **Take things gradually.** Give yourself time to warm up to the big changes you are facing.
- **Share your feelings** with your partner. Let her help you sort them out.
- **Laugh.** You can always find something funny in any situation if you try. And sometimes the toughest things you go through are also the most amusing in retrospect.
- **Do something creative** to break out of the doldrums. Get out the camera and get some pictures of your new family developed and framed and put them up around the house.
- **Stay involved.** When exhaustion and frustration set in, everything in you wants to back off. You need to do the opposite. When you feel most like tuning out, push yourself to take the baby for a walk or give your partner a back rub. Soon you will find that overcoming your own resistance becomes easier and more gratifying.
- **Get away.** Spend time together on a date or even overnight with your mate.

Kick Back With Your Friends

Standard procedure for new fathers is to give up the few friends we have (a) because they foster anti-social behavior and (b) they are not interested in the color of our baby's poop. The bottom line is that we get isolated and cooped up just when we need to get out and de-stress. Your buddies provide balance in your life, especially when the pressure builds. So if you are feeling it, for the sake of your family, call up your friends and go out and have a beer. Review the sports section first so you have something to talk about besides the baby. It works a lot better if they have babies or kids themselves, as a little appreciation of your circumstances and semi-heroic efforts can do wonders for your attitude.

Connect With Other Dads

Take a page out of the new mom's playbook and network with the dads you know and connect with some new ones. Although they are a good bet, don't limit yourself to the mates of new moms your wife met in your childbirth class. Try your own father – you may be surprised by how much you have in common. Take your baby to go see your brother, or ask the guy down the hall at work or the one sitting next to you on the plane about their kids.

Getting together with some other dads can quickly put you back on solid ground with a fresh head of steam. The veterans who do this uniformly report it to be both reassuring and motivating. If someone gushes about how wonderful everything has been since his baby's birth, explain the rules: points are only awarded for get-it-off-your-chest gripes and screw ups, and worst case scenarios win.

Dads Can Get Depressed Too

It can get you down too – at least 30% of new fathers experience significant depression due to all the stress they face and the enormity, speed and velocity of the changes occurring in their lives. If this happens to you, recognize it for what it is, understand it is normal, and deal with it constructively. Keep in mind that worrying about responsibility means you are on the job, and take comfort in the fact that men who do their job as fathers end up happier, healthier and more self respecting. Talk to your physician or another professional to make sure you get it handled.

 I felt pressured to always be there for my new family and play Superdad, never thinking that I needed time every once in a while to recuperate and refuel my daddy tank.

- Veteran Dad

THE IMPACT OF FATHERHOOD ON MEN

So what is it like once you have experience as a father under your belt? We have oriented you to the problems that can occur, but you should be ready for the upside as well. You will have to experience it yourself to really understand, but here is our best shot at describing it.

A Glimpse of Your Future

At *Boot Camp* workshops, "veteran" dads bring and take care of their babies and explain what they have learned after two to four months. What the rookies see in these men is confidence, pride, a sense of purpose, and excitement for the future. They are honest about how tough it can be, but these are upbeat fathers, men on a mission and full of potential.

You Will Transform Into a Dad

Over time we gradually develop a new, stronger sense of ourselves as fathers (a cross between a pack horse and a lion.) As we learn to meet our babies' needs, we come to trust our instincts, just as moms do. And as we become comfortable in raising our children and helping them learn new things, we develop a deep awareness of how important we are to them and a sense of validation as dads. While this transformation into a father clearly occurs in the circumstances of our lives, it ultimately takes place in the depths of our own minds. This is where we develop the extraordinary commitment and drive necessary to not only do the job, but to excel.

Your Child Offers You a Great Deal

Little can compare to a child's love, your baby falling asleep in your arms, comforting a daughter scared by a nightmare, or a son's delight over knocking down the block tower you helped him build. No matter what happens in the rest of our life, we are always special to our child. We can tell you that as a deep and rich relationship with your child develops, you will experience an unparalleled sense of purpose and manhood that fills your heart and soul and fulfills the core of your being. It will have a broad, pervasive impact upon you that gives real and deep meaning to your life.

You Will Become a Better Man

Becoming enmeshed in caring for a baby on turf owned by women (for millenniums) can feel emasculating at first, but we end up carving out our turf and figuring out how to do it our own way. We also learn taking care of a sick baby through the night is not for wimps, and that protecting and providing for a family requires a great deal of strength. Raising children brings out the best in us and spurs us to mature and excel as human beings. The pride and fulfillment we experience by doing this challenging job feeds our hearts and souls. We become men in the finest sense of the term.

Closer Relationship With Our Own Father

By becoming a father, we take on a very special role that we share with our own father. Many of us report this provides the basis for a new relationship with him. Consider talking with your father about his experience as a new father, and when his grandchild arrives, find a private moment to hand him the baby with a "congratulations, gramps!"

Take Pride in All That You Do

One of the paradoxes of fatherhood is that the best among us worry most about the job we are doing. We focus on our mistakes in order to learn from them, and then take on the next challenge a growing child sends our way. We should periodically reflect on the changes in our life and take pride in the fact we are delivering on an extraordinary commitment to our child and family.

> **"** *I fear that I might get too wrapped up in my work and career and not be there for my family. Not spending enough time to bond with my child is of great concern to me.*
>
> *- Rookie Dad* **"**

Work Options	Implications & Ideas	What It Means To Your Family
Workaholic, Road Warrior, Deploy Away From Home	The reality may be you need to work more to pay the bills, or meet essential career demands or military obligations. If you make your time at home with your family count, this can work for a couple of years. Make sure working more is not just an excuse to get away from the stress at home.	You are providing essential economic support, especially if it allows mom to stay home, but your family will mostly be without the benefit of a dad. You will miss out as well, so you will need an exit strategy. See page 5-E for ideas on how to make your time away from home count too.
Cut Back On Long Hours or Work Partly From Home	Some employers are responding with flexible schedules and telecommuting to fathers' desires to spend time with their children. You will need to request or even push for these options. Many fathers also find they are able to work more efficiently in order to spend more time at home.	Work flexibility and working less nights and weekends will allow you many more opportunities to interact with your child and support mom. Working at home requires discipline on your part, and it is hard to actually care for a child when doing so, but you get to be there for your family.
Find Less Demanding Job	Backing off on your career aspirations is a sacrifice, but finding another job with fewer hours, perhaps in the same company, may be your best option. In addition to time, stress is also a factor as we tend to bring it home, so reducing stress is as important as reducing work hours.	This likely involves a decrease in pay as well as a serious increase in your fulfillment as a father. Research is clear on the benefits babies receive from having dad around, and it brings much appreciated balance to mom's life as well. Start by talking with her about the trade-offs.
Reduce Commute Time	Moving closer to work or finding a job closer to home will result in less time on the road and more time with your family. Easier said than done of course, but check out the possibilities; a family-friendly neighborhood or even a less demanding job may a so be part of the ceal.	The time you save can be considerable, and it is prime time in the morning and early evening when your child is awake and ready to go. The commitment it takes to make these kinds of changes reflects a real dad who gets it and starts off in a strong position to make the most of it.
Set Up Business At Home	It involves risks, but if successful, it is a great combination of a good income, no commute and a flexible schedule that enables you to optimize your time on the home front. It requires personal discipline and practical steps like a separate work area, but it can bring balance to your new life.	A great option if you can pull it off, as you pay the bills and are able to fully participate in your children's upbringing. There are business risks, but overhead is low and this is a great way to go when the kids are young. Be careful that business stress does not diminish you as a dad.
Work Part Time	Most new families have two working parents and in many mom is a major income generator. This enables more men to work part time and become the major care giver to their babies supported by part-time day care. A part time job can also counteract the boredom inherent in full time baby care.	The alternative is two parents working full time, which tends to be very stressful for new families. Part time work can involve cutting down on hours at your current job, starting a home-based business, or finding a part time job. Work out the best possible arrangement with mom.
Be A Stay At Home Dad	Staying at home to raise your child may be one of the most rewarding things you ever do. It also may not work for you, especially if your motivation is to get out of a lousy job. Don't doubt your ability though: 150,000 dads stayed home in 2004 and many more would join them if they could.	You will be the most important influence in your child's life. Traditional norms of dad as breadwinner are dissipating along with social pressures stay-at-home dads experience. Take a professional approach to make the most of this opportunity or you may find it boring and demeaning.

INVOLVEMENT & BALANCE   **+**

STRATEGIES FOR WHEN YOUR TIME IS SHORT

Parenthood often comes at a time in a man's life when he has to work 60-hour weeks, and some dads believe they can make up for lost time later. The truth is, you can't. The first three years of your child's life are the most vital in shaping who he will become later in life. You will never have other opportunities like those when your child is an infant, so make sure that you do spend time — even if it's just a couple of hours a week — alone with your baby now.

Dealing With Economic Realities

Of course, today's economic realities create difficult circumstances. Many careers demand long work hours, your new baby will add to your financial requirements, and your mate is going to be out of commission as an income generator for at least a little while. Taking a month off when your baby is born may be as much an option as going to the moon. Even making sure you're available for the birth itself may be difficult.

Many veterans faced such circumstances, and you can learn from their ideas:

- Do everything you can to assure you are there for the birth. Missing the birth will be the biggest regret that you have.
- Change that first diaper. Make the time you do have count as much as possible. Set the tone that you are here to be a player and get involved early.
- Strive for solutions that enable you to spend time with your child. Be creative. Figure out how to work from home; even once a week is better than nothing.
- Play a strong role in providing emotional support for mom (such as calling her from work and emailing her; ask how she is doing or let her know how proud you are of her).
- When you are home, spend time alone with your baby. Don't let your limited experience as a care giver interfere. Send mom out with some friends and just do it.
- If you simply have no choice, do not allow yourself to feel diminished because you can't spend lots of time with your new child. Your work and income is your family's lifeline.

It will probably be an ongoing challenge for you and your family. Two-thirds of fathers report that they would spend more time at home with their children if they were financially able to do so.

When You Spend a Lot of Time Away From Home

Spending time away from your little one can be tough, especially when you're talking a week or even a month at a time. Travel for long periods, as for military personnel, can be depressing. It's important to stay focused on why we work in the first place – to provide for our families. Even if your involvement with your child is minimal, it's important to make sure that involvement is as meaningful as possible:

- Play with your baby before you leave in the morning and just after you get home. Many dads report that their babies sleep longer if they play with them at night.
- Keep his picture where you see it often, and keep him in mind while you're on the road.
- Call mom often and get the lowdown on junior's antics and accomplishments for the day.
- Enlist mom, who can send you pictures and recordings and hold the phone to your baby's ear so you can talk to him, or show him his daddy on a cell phone picture.
- Get creative. A young father recently deployed to Iraq tape recorded a dozen nursery rhymes that his wife plays for their baby so that he will recognize dad's voice when he gets back home.

Also, remember the pioneering dads of a decade ago who had the courage to tell their boss they were going to cut back on their time in the office to spend more time at home; they opened a door for the rest of us.

　I usually take over when I get home from work, but I'm tired and it takes a lot of patience not to become short-tempered with the baby.
- Veteran Dad

PREPARING TO BECOME A FATHER

A Great Time to Become a Dad

You could not have picked a better or more challenging time to become a dad. Fatherhood is coming out of a century long slump, and the driving force is dads who simply want to provide their children the close bond they wish they had with their own father. The downside of fathers who were not part of their kid's lives is also very clear to us, and we are not about to let it happen to our kids, or to ourselves.

Dads today are bringing a strong commitment to raising children, and this in turn is creating new respect for the importance of all fathers. It is also opening doors and creating opportunities for new fathers, as well raising the bar for you regarding your involvement with your child. While our job today is tougher in some respects, the payoff in terms of being close to our kids is priceless, and it fuels our drive to get the job done.

How Do You Prepare?

Expecting moms are motivated by a baby growing inside them, major hormonal changes and decades of socialization, all while being supported by a committed network of mothers, medical services and the publishing industry; all you have is your expecting wife. If you are lucky, you have a friend who recently became a father you can talk to. And if you are smart, you will talk to such friends and make new ones to find out what you are getting into. Other suggestions:

Connect With Other Dads

As we have demonstrated for almost two decades, we can learn a great deal from each other. The problem is, for the most part, dads-to-be don't ask, and experienced fathers don't tell – unless asked. Break the ice and talk to other dads and request their suggestions and advice. They may be caught a little off guard because no one asked before, but it's a great way to both complement a man and learn from his experience.

- ☐ Go to a childbirth and baby care class, and *Boot Camp for New Dads* (or other) if available.
- ☐ Read up; cruise your wife's books and make use of books and videos for fathers.
- ☐ Count on going through rough patches. If you don't, you are either very lucky or you are not trying hard enough.
- ☐ Assess your feelings and work through them. Get past issues such as "not being ready to have a child," because they will preclude a focus on getting prepared.
- ☐ No matter your worries, be pro-active in getting ready. This will minimize worries.

A Process With Ups and Downs

Becoming a dad doesn't happen overnight. While the learning curve is sharp at first, it tapers off and extends for decades. You have a nine month warm up period, hell week lasts from one to three months, and then you'll find your groove. Becoming a dad is an intensely personal process that includes doubts and frustrations along with peak times when she smiles and you feel like a billion. Focus on getting past those first months, and then work out a course for the long term.

You May Need to Stand Your Ground

Make sure you and mom are clear on your plans for being an involved father. It's not uncommon for a new mom to be so immersed in the baby that she becomes a "gatekeeper" restricting dad's participation. If this happens, be patient and understanding, but make sure you are not pushed out of your child's life. Ditto with your mother-in-law, boss, and friends. Many men who worked hard to provide for their families have been surprised to find out down the road that they weren't really a part of their children's lives.

Prepare for the Worst and the Best

Becoming a father can be very tough. We don't sugar coat it; we tell it like it is for a lot of men, which is how it might be for you. Or it might not. If you assume that all the hard stuff you hear or read about will happen to you, then you are getting it wrong. Nobody gets hit with all of it; just be ready for whatever comes your way, good or bad, because either way, you will want to make the best of it.

Starting Point: Our Own Fathers

Some of our fathers were great, some weren't there at all, and stepfathers, grandfathers, or other men may have taken on the job. Their legacy is our starting point for becoming a dad. Even a distant or absent father can benefit us now, since the more we missed out as children, the more desire we bring to the job. Having a father who showed you how to be a real dad is huge. A great way to start your own journey is to reflect on theirs.

 We were sitting around the fire at an Indian Princess campout and we started talking about our girls. I was relieved that my worries were minor compared to some of the guys, and inspired that no matter what they were dealing with, there was nothing they would not do for their daughters.
- *Veteran Dad*

COMMON FEARS AND CONCERNS

After hearing the news of a baby on the way, you may experience doubt, fear, second thoughts, even panic. No matter what's going on inside, you are far from alone. Much of this is mind games caused by rapid, fundamental change in your life. At the risk of giving you more to worry about, here's a sample of some things soon-to-be fathers think about:

✓ What am I getting into?
✓ This was not my choice.
✓ I don't even like babies.
✓ I'm not ready/I won't be a good father.
✓ I'll throw up in the delivery room.
✓ I'll blow it as a birthing coach.
✓ I'll drop the baby.
✓ I'll lose a great life.

✓ I'll lose a great wife.
✓ Can she handle this?
✓ How much pain will she be in?
✓ What if there are complications?
✓ Will she ever get back to normal?
✓ Will she be a good mother?
✓ I can't afford a bigger house, another car.
✓ How much is baby stuff going to cost?

✓ I work 60 hours now/how can I pay the bills and spend the time with our baby?
✓ We barely make it now, and she wants to stay home.
✓ When will my sex life return?
✓ My mother-in-law is a nightmare.
✓ Is this baby really mine?
✓ I just want him to come out.

So if you find your emotions ranging from euphoria to dread, take a deep breath and remember it is normal. This will allow you to focus constructively on the real challenges you foresee. Check off or note your concerns as a first step.

Your Life Will Change – But How?

We generally have a full life before our first baby comes along. Our careers are usually building or are already in full swing. We have fulfilling relationships with our mates, spending time together and sharing common interests. We have friends, hobbies, outside activities, or physical endeavors that fill up our days. In many cases, long work hours have already stretched our time to the limit. You will hear that your life as you know it is over. But what does this mean?

Fathers of 1-year-olds will tell you they were surprised at how much work is involved. And that's on top of their already busy life. In essence, becoming a dad means having more things to do than the time to do it, so while you work harder, you have to cut back on the things you now enjoy. You also have to make choices between competing priorities. You may want to take several weeks off without pay when the baby comes while one of your major concerns is how you are going to pay for all of this. There has to be a reward for this, otherwise men wouldn't do it, and 40 million men in the U.S. alone do.

Babies Do Change Relationships-Many for the Better

New babies strengthen the love and respect of about one-third of new parents who together overcome the challenges and share the rewards of building a family. About half find their relationship suffers; they were uninformed and unprepared for the impacts of a new baby, and then once theirs arrived, they were unable to communicate and work out their issues.

No matter how much two people love each other, the process of becoming a family can polarize you and your mate. Differences in values, backgrounds, personalities, and concerns sharpen as the demands of an infant press down on you. No issue is more important to a child and his parents than their relationship, so a major investment in making it work is warranted. You need to be proactive on this because mom will be focused on the baby. Set aside time to discuss your priorities in raising your child, how you want to work together, and how you will handle the inevitable conflicts that arise.

How to Handle Sympathy Pains or "Couvade"

If you experience unusual nausea, major weight gain, insomnia, or food cravings that mimic your mate's symptoms, it is likely that you are experiencing sympathy pains (couvade syndrome). While your friends may rag on you, the net result is you will likely be a better dad:

☐ Men who share symptoms with their mate report feeling close and connected to her and the baby, perhaps in a spiritual sense, and that she appreciated his "sharing" her pregnancy. (Mother's reports can differ, e.g., "he needed attention".)

☐ Couvade syndrome is now thought to be triggered by biochemical and hormonal changes that occur in dads-to-be.

☐ Research shows that men who experience couvade are pre-disposed to spend more time caring for their babies.

Couvade syndrome starts up at the end of the first trimester and ends with birth. If you experience couvade, take a positive view and remember all that will be left when your baby arrives is your pre-disposition to be a great dad. (P.S.: the record for men is a beer belly that mimics mom's at 7 months.)

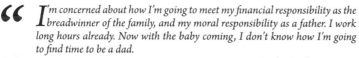

I'm concerned about how I'm going to meet my financial responsibility as the breadwinner of the family, and my moral responsibility as a father. I work long hours already. Now with the baby coming, I don't know how I'm going to find time to be a dad.

- Rookie Dad

RESEARCH: OUR CHILDREN NEED US TO BE MEN

Do Fathers Matter? We Have Come a Long Way Re: Our Babies

For two decades we have witnessed researchers' views of fathers evolve. They have observed their quarry – dads like us - up close and personal in our own natural habitat. Early on, many reported fathers were uninvolved with their babies and were of little value in comparison to moms. This didn't seem right, particularly as we walked our crying baby to sleep once again. Yeah, we struggled at times, but it seemed like no matter what we did, we were being judged based upon the worst among us.

Research Catches Up

Over the past decade the researchers have caught up with the tremendous changes driven by the many dads on the job. They have concluded that we are not only involved, as dads we can have unique and profoundly positive impacts upon our children, and we are endowed by nature to both defend our families from threats and cherish and care for our kids from birth. They are also pursuing the notion that, like moms, millenniums of evolution and socialization have a significant effect on how we act when we become fathers.

Our Children Need Us

Research catalogued by the National Fatherhood Initiative indicates that children whose fathers are a consistent, positive force in their lives do better socially, intellectually, and on a broad range of other factors ranging from economic status in childhood to peer relationships in adolescence, to productivity as adults. Other research findings include:

- ☐ Children of involved fathers manage stress better during their school years and enjoy improved physical well being, perceptual abilities, positive relationships, self-control and ability to take the initiative.
- ☐ A close, warm relationship with our daughters strengthens their feelings of competence and sense of femininity.
- ☐ The love and care of mom and dad have an equal impact on their child's well-being, happiness and academic success.
- ☐ A father's love and care are the major factors in combating a child's problems with conduct, delinquency or substance abuse, and an involved father's children are less likely be subject to the breakup of their family, poverty, teen pregnancy, violence or abuse.

Not only are we hugely important to our children, we have a big job ahead of us.

They Need Us To Be Ourselves

Of all the powerful and complex dynamics in the circle of life, a father's critical role in teaching his baby to play has got to be one of the coolest. Research has found that despite the obvious advantages moms enjoy in terms of baby appeal, two-thirds of 6 month-old babies choose dad when it comes to playtime. Fathers, perhaps due in part to maturity issues, are naturally designed to be her perfect playmate. Tickling, flight lessons, peek-a-boo and wrestling all come naturally. Playing is also bonding at its finest. Dads elicit radiant smiles and infectious belly laughs, sometimes with just a wink. And finally, playing is your baby's main job: it teaches him how to laugh and take risks, it develops his motor skills and speeds the development of his brain and nervous system. It's a dirty job, but remember when you are crawling on the floor, barking like a dog as you chase him around, it's dad's job.

They Need Us To Be Men

There are times in our child's life when we really need to step up and it may come early:

- ☐ Premature babies make initial life as a parent very stressful, and their smiles are delayed.
- ☐ A baby experiencing serious colic seems to go on a crying jag for the first three months.
- ☐ Babies born by caesarean incapacitate mom for weeks, leaving dad with a double load.
- ☐ Fathers of twins, triplets, etc., have to step up big time.

For those that do, the rewards come early too, as the research shows that by being there when their child really needed them, they formed a stronger connection and were more engaged in caring for their baby at 5 months and on.

" When I walk in from work, she knows its playtime.

- Veteran Dad "

RESEARCH: BIOCHEMICAL CHANGES HELP DRIVE US FORWARD

More of Us Are Doing the Job and We Have Raised the Bar for All Dads

The research is clear: we dads are getting what we want, we like it, and our children do too. A random survey conducted by the National Center of Education Statistics (NCES) of 6,300 fathers with 9 month-old babies at home found that:

- 80% rated themselves as "better than average or very good," 17% average; only 2% had some trouble as a father.
- 99% "agreed that fatherhood is a highly rewarding experience," 84% strongly agreed and only 1% disagreed.
- 96% engaged in some type of physical play with their baby daily.
- 87% changed at least a few diapers each week.
- 90% take their baby with them on errands once or twice a week.
- 100% find holding and cuddling their child is fun, with 85% finding this to be the case all the time.

We Often Start Out Way Behind the Curve

The same NCES study, however, also found that at conception, 25% had not wanted the pregnancy to occur at all and another 19% did not feel ready and wished it had occurred later. Most came around as the stats above show, and they did by getting with the program early on: 95% saw the ultrasound, 97% felt their baby move, and 93% attended the birth. Participation in Boot Camp for New Dads is also expanding, which is a good thing because expectations of new fathers, and particularly our expectations of ourselves, is growing too. In essence, we have a lot more ground to cover than our dads had to cover, between the time we hear "I'm pregnant!" and the time our baby is born.

Biochemical Changes Help Drive Us Forward

Hormones have gotten a bum rap due to their impacts upon women, but they serve a purpose, and research indicates we experience some changes as well in the weeks before and after the birth. And like boosting our testosterone and endorphins with exercise, we can help them kick in and harness their power to enhance our experience and capabilities as fathers. Researchers have found:

- A doubling of the stress hormone cortisol in the 3 weeks before birth. It intensifies our feelings and response to our baby's cries, and also fuels our fight or flight impulse, which explains our heightened protective instinct.
- A 20% increase in prolactin in the weeks before birth, which likely enhances our instincts to care for our baby.
- A 33% drop in testosterone in the 3 weeks after birth, and a bounce back to normal at 4-7 weeks. Beyond temporarily diminishing our sex drive, this enables a strong emotional focus on our baby during this prime bonding period.

Apparently we are biologically predisposed to care for our child as well as pull him from a burning building. The key to taking advantage is to stay close to mom during pregnancy (which triggers our changes), and then take advantage of them by quickly getting hands-on in caring for our baby. In fact, starting with holding our baby for the first time, most fathers have an intuitive feeling that something in them has changed, and this new research validates decades of such feelings.

The Months Surrounding the Birth Provides Us a Window of Opportunity

Princeton's Center for Research on Child-Wellbeing found that virtually all new fathers want to be a good father, and the months surrounding the child's birth are a window of opportunity during which fathers are most receptive to support and change. This dovetails with the new research above documenting our biological drivers during this period, and helps explain the success of *Boot Camp for New Dads*, which reaches men early and provides them the orientation that enables them to "hit the ground crawling" when their child arrives.

We Have Unique and Profound Impacts

Kyle Pruett, MD, author of *Fatherneed* (2000), explains "why a father has so powerful an influence on the kind of person his child eventually becomes." In his first chapter, "Fathers Do Not Mother," a key conclusion was that a father and his infant develop an enhanced relationship through interactions that occur between them "in the absence of the mother." This one-on-one time is when dads develop a broad range of skills for engaging their infants, who in turn benefit from richer social and exploratory behavior, smile more frequently and more often present toys to their dads.

> " *Hey guys, can we stop talking about MOM? Hey, I don't know about you guys but I'm riding an emotional roller coaster too!*
> *- Rookie Dad* "

DEAR MOMS-TO-BE, LOVE DADS

Since 1990 we have worked together to learn how to do our best as new dads and pass it on to the next guy. In every workshop, new fathers tell dads-to-be the most important thing is to "take care of mom." Not just during birth, but initially during the tough parts of pregnancy, and particularly once the baby arrives.

Over the years, supporting mom morphed into understanding mom, respecting and appreciating mom, giving mom a break from being mom, helping mom get balance in her life, getting her to come back home once she does (just kidding), and reconnecting as a couple once we settle in with a new baby.

It occurred to us that you may want to know some things about new dads, so here is our best shot. We even wrote you a love letter!

Dear Moms-to-be,

With a baby on the way, you are hearing a lot from all directions. But we dads are the ones who love moms and are in it for the long haul, and we have some things to say too. So, a few months after your baby arrives and you have settled into momhood, remember these thoughts about us dads.

Giving birth is awesome, but we find the overall metamorphosis you go through as you become a mom is even more so. Your commitment to our baby is unconditional and virtually limitless. We would not be the least bit surprised to see a mother pick up the front of a truck that just ran over her baby's stroller.

We don't understand all that is going on with you, or even ourselves, and suspect you may be just as confused. We should talk more. This is more your specialty, so maybe you could help us out here.

We think you moms should go easy on yourselves. It seems like some new demand "for the good of the baby" is made upon you daily, and you will feel guilty if you don't do it. We could probably help you out here; we are pretty good about blowing off the small stuff.

You need to know that we dads are very important to our babies too, so your understanding of us is also essential. While not as dramatically as you, we are transforming as well. Although we fight it at times, fatherhood brings out the best in us, and is about love, sacrifice, dignity, respect and honor - factors that as men we thrive on. So don't be surprised when we pick up the back end of that truck.

Finally, we miss you. It is not that we don't understand the new demands you face as a mom or don't enjoy being a dad, it is just that we miss you and what we had together when there were just two of us. This reflects our feelings for you and is a good thing, but we are not sure what to do about it.

Together we are doing something truly momentous and challenging, and no one can encourage us more as parents than each other. When two people who have it coming from all directions are covering each other's back, they develop an even stronger relationship. This is our plan. Can you imagine anything better for our kids?

Love, Dads

Our Moms Advisory Board

Moms are our best supporters and when we asked several to help us with advice for moms-to-be, they had some zingers:

"Men are not mind readers; if we want something, we should tell them what it is."

"If I knew then what I know now, I would not have tried to do it all myself. I can't, and my baby needs his dad."

"Get him out with the baby on his own. It can be scary at first, for him too, but they come back in one piece. And happy!"

"Buy him a backpack for the baby. When he walks along with his baby strapped on, he puffs out his chest and feels all proud and manly. It is like he is showing her off and protecting her at the same time."

"He will do things with the baby differently than you, and if you insist he does it your way, you'll find yourself doing it all."

"Be patient. We get way ahead of them when we're carrying the baby, networking with other moms and getting inundated with magazines, books, etc. The guys have to figure it out on their own, but they eventually catch up."

"Don't let your love life go, even if you're tired and frustrated over baby issues; it is the glue that holds you together."

 My wife still feels she does things better but we're very good at divvying up duties. Our care of the baby is very different - methods are different - results are the same.

- Veteran Dad

MOM: HELP HIM GET A GOOD START AS A DAD

Respect His Role As a Father: Babies Need Their Dads

Research indicates that children whose fathers are a consistent, positive force in their lives do better socially, intellectually, and in a broad range of other factors ranging from economic status in childhood to peer relationships in adolescence to productivity as adults. A dad has a unique and profound influence on the person his baby eventually becomes; e.g., his natural roughhousing develops her motor skills, speeds the development of her brain and nervous system and teaches her how to take risks. A connected, involved dad will help make your child healthier, happier and more emotionally secure.

Mom Plays a Critical Role in How Involved Dad Becomes

You can encourage and facilitate his involvement with his baby, or inadvertently hinder it through "gatekeeping." Multiple studies have shown that "mothers who believe that men can be good parents, that children need an involved father, and that men should participate in childcare are more likely to have partners who display these qualities." Moms who respect their mate as a father, help him get up to speed, and encourage his strong connection with his baby are rewarded with a dad who does his best for his child and a parenting partner who brings much needed balance to her life as a mom.

Encourage Him to Connect With His Baby Before Birth

Your bond is naturally hardwired. A dad-to-be needs to build his. It's critical he builds a strong one because the bond with his child is what will motivate him to make the sacrifices required of a new father. Encourage him to start early in your pregnancy; Page 1-C provides proven ideas on how he can do so.

Understand This is a Challenging Time for Him

This isn't his father's fatherhood. More is expected of him and he wants to be part of his child's life, but he may have had no real role model. Preparing to be a father can be a confusing time, filled with concerns or fears he may have no one to share with. He may not want to burden you with his worries, especially when you are facing much more obvious challenges. Ask him about his feelings and concerns, let him vent and let him know you care.

Encourage Him To Do It, And Do It His Way

As a new mom, you may develop a possessive focus on "your" baby and distrust dad to care for the child or insist he do it "your" way. This may cause dad to lose (or never gain) confidence and actually back away from taking care of his own baby. Realizing that fathers take a different approach, and that in doing so we equip our babies with new strengths, you should not only let him do it his way, but help him find a special thing he does with the baby – baths, walks, etc.

Get the Romance Back After You Weather the Storm

Once your roller coaster life with a newborn settles down, you and dad need to refocus on each other. Otherwise, your relationship will suffer for years, which is what happens to about half of new parents after their first baby arrives. Don't let the demands and frustrations you face as a new mom spoil your love life. It naturally takes a big hit due to pregnancy and birth, and often goes to the bottom of the priority list. Don't underestimate its value to him no matter how understanding he says he is; in fact the less frequent, the more important it becomes to him. Strengthening your marriage is the best thing you can both do for your child, as well as yourselves. So get those weekly dates going and bring the romance back.

Your Efforts with Dad Can Have a Big Payoff

Fatherhood can bring out the best in him as a man and make him your family's "Knight in Shining Armor." Helping him get a good start will make his early experience as a father enjoyable, which will motivate him to do his best.

> **❝** *Talk to your wife about how you feel. That you're feeling neglected. That as much as she needs to know that you love her, you need her to do the same. Make sure that your relationship stays strong. It doesn't always have to be about the baby.*
>
> *- Veteran Dad* **❞**

Notes

Notes

GETTING YOUR LOVE LIFE BACK

Let's face it: as a new dad, pent up sexual frustration can make you come on like a bull in heat. The trouble is, your wife needs you to be patient and romance her first. Coming on too strong will be highly counterproductive.

Don't Push Her: When it comes to romance, applying too much pressure on your partner to get things back on track will backfire.

Cuddle: She has a lot of physical contact with a demanding baby and may not want any more at first. Take it slow and give her a foot rub, back rub, some hugs, and spoon.

Go to Bed Together: Just having a little window of private time goes a long way. You can use it to chat, snuggle, or whatever else feels right.

Schedule Dates: They don't always work due to changing priorities and intrusions, but if nothing is scheduled you may never get around to it. Take the initiative to schedule the dates and handle arrangements (sitter, etc.).

Sex in Six Weeks to Six Months

Most doctors say that six weeks after a normal vaginal delivery, she should be good to go. Actually, she'll be good to go when she is physically ready, and when she feels like it. That is, she is ready if she's feeling rested, good about her baby, good about her body, and good about you. This could take a while.

The New Rules of Foreplay: Quadruple your standard foreplay timeframe to give her plenty of time to warm up and push all thoughts of the baby out of her mind. Try a long massage. Start at her feet and slowly work your way up.

Relearn What She Likes: Pregnancy and nursing may have changed your wife's hotspots. Go with what her body responds to, not with your old playbook.

Learn Bedroom Finesse – Maybe for the First Time: Most guys aren't exactly Don Juan in bed. If you want her to enjoy herself as much as possible, you may need to learn how to really turn her on. Men's magazines are full of advice and ads for better sex videos.

Get Away: An overnight trip + a romantic location not too far from home + a trusted babysitter = sexual nirvana. Make sure the sitter can reach you if need be. If mom's breastfeeding, don't forget the pump.

The First Time

Making love for the first time after having a baby is generally awkward, and often uncomfortable. It might be funny, but the odds are against it being hot. Make sure she's ready, rested, and relaxed. Tell her she looks beautiful. Start with a gentle massage, kissing and hugging. Most important, take your time and be gentle.

Talk it through beforehand. Let her know that you care, and want to know what she thinks will work best.

Make it a special event, a milestone for your new relationship as parents by doing it up right. If flowers were ever appropriate, this is the time.

Set the stage. Make sure the baby is handled, soft music, a candle and perhaps a little wine will help.

Lubrication often is necessary, so keep some within reach.

Be careful around her breasts. They can be very tender from the baby's vigorous sucking.

Keep her comfortable. Go slow and use positions that let her control the action (mom on top).

Keep expectations low and be flexible; your objective should be basic lovemaking and nothing more.

If it becomes painful, of course, stop, and hold off until another day.

Consider non-coital alternatives, use your imaginations.

Make it an act of love, no matter what happens. End it on a high note.

Simple Ways to Remind Her You Love Her

1. Quick phone calls: "Just wanted to hear your voice."
2. Email: "Had some good news and wanted you to be the first to know."
3. Love notes left where she will find them at home.
4. Give her a quick neck rub in the morning.
5. Go for a walk and hold her hand.
6. When you come home from work, give her a kiss, then take the baby.
7. Buy her flowers.
8. Put up pictures of her and the baby around the house.

> **"** *If you ever want to have sex again with your wife, make sure she gets plenty of rest.*
>
> *- Veteran Dad* **"**

4 Caring for Mom

ROMANCING A NEW MOM

After two to three months your roller coaster life with a newborn will probably be settling down. This is a time for you and mom to refocus on each other. Since she will likely be preoccupied with the baby, the ball is in your court to take the initiative on establishing the relationship you want for the next decade.

☐ **Understand that You are Starting Over:** Re-kindling the romance in your relationship is a lot like starting on a fresh courtship. It can take time.

☐ **Communication is Critical:** Talking is how we sort out and resolve problems, and several months after the birth, the stack of issues can be high. Talking can also evolve into verbal foreplay…*sometimes*.

☐ **Tell Her Your Dreams:** And ask about hers. Talking together about your future, remembering your pre-baby past, and sharing your dreams brings the two of you closer.

☐ **Encourage and Respect Her as a Mom:** Nothing, not even getting back to a size eight, will be as important to her self-esteem as the job she is doing as a mom.

☐ **Do Your Part as a Father:** She is now viewing you as her baby's father. When she watches you giving him a bath or rocking him to sleep on your chest, she sees a happy baby and a **hot dad** (see "verbal foreplay" under *Communication is Critical* above!).

☐ **Give Her Time Alone:** While with the baby she is on call for his slightest need or demand. This means she will need some time for herself. Make sure she gets it. If possible, get her out with her girlfriends.

☐ **Get Out Together With Your Baby on Weekends:** Go on a date with mom and your baby—to a sporting event, the zoo, or just out for a walk.

☐ **Engage in Adult Conversation:** Help break up her isolation by asking her about anything other than the baby (current events, her pre-baby interests, what's going on with friends, etc).

☐ **Help Her Re-Engage Her Mind:** Encourage her to read a novel, go to a movie or take up a hobby; anything that broadens her horizons beyond the baby.

☐ **Eat Together:** As simple as it sounds, it's a great way to begin reconnecting with your partner. Prepare a gourmet dinner together and start a tradition for your new family.

☐ **Exercise Together:** A mom who gets regular exercise is a happier mom. Getting exercise together by walking (or jogging or bike riding) with your baby is a great idea.

☐ **Bring Out the List:** Remember the list you made during her pregnancy, of things you like to do together? It's time to bring it out, pick one of the items and do it. Post the list on the refrigerator to remind you both that regular "mom and dad" time is essential.

 4 Caring for Mom

Six Characteristics of Happy Parents

Researchers found couples who successfully overcame the polarizing effects of a first baby shared six key characteristics:

1. Surrender individual goals and work together as a team.
2. Resolve differences about division of labor and argue constructively.
3. Keep common interests despite priorities that are branching off in different directions.
4. Understand their marriage will never be quite the same after the baby's arrival.
5. Continue communicating in a manner that sustains and supports the marriage.
6. Each handles frustration in a way that does not overstress their partner or their marriage.

> ❝ *It's the little things that are important, like when you walk into the house after work, always kiss her first and maybe give her some flowers. That will reassure her that she is every bit of a woman that she has ever been even though she is a mother.*
>
> *- Veteran Dad*

BABY BLUES & POSTPARTUM DEPRESSION

The Baby Blues

The baby blues generally occur between birth and 6 weeks, and about 80% of new moms experience them in some way. A drop in hormone levels following delivery can be aggravated by being overly tired, going back to work, feeling inadequate as a mom, feeling trapped/isolated and problems in bonding with the baby. Symptoms include mood swings, anxiety, irritability, insomnia, crying, nervousness, and general unhappiness. Once mom and baby settle into a routine (after several weeks), and her hormone levels stabilize, the baby blues usually disappear.

What You Can Do

Your job is to remain supportive and find ways to lighten her load. Encourage her to talk about what is going on and remind her it's normal and will pass. Insist she get out of the house and away from the baby. If the problems persist some professional help may be in order, so talk to your physician. It's paramount to take care of emotional problems quickly because once they become more entrenched these problems will be even more difficult to deal with.

Postpartum Depression

Up to 20% of new mothers develop full blown postpartum depression, which typically occurs between six weeks and one year after childbirth. This is a medical problem, and women with a family or personal history of depression are more likely to suffer from it. If some of the following symptoms persist for more than a week notify your spouse's obstetrician or a helpline at the hospital immediately and discuss your concerns:

- ✓ Insomnia or sleeping too much
- ✓ A lack of interest in activities
- ✓ Lethargy or hyperactivity
- ✓ Hopelessness or lack of control
- ✓ Loss of appetite or overeating
- ✓ Inability to concentrate
- ✓ Feelings of helplessness
- ✓ Inability to care for herself or baby
- ✓ Panic attacks
- ✓ Extreme mood swings
- ✓ Disorientation and confusion
- ✓ Loss of touch with reality

What You Can Do

As a new father it is extremely important to know the signs of depression. You will have to take action on your mate's behalf if you suspect that she is slipping beyond the baby blues into true postpartum depression. Because of mom's isolation at home, you may be the only one to even notice these symptoms. She is ill and requires medical attention; essential steps to take are:

- Take care of your baby and consider asking for help from friends and relatives.
- Immediately consult professional help for your wife by an experienced counselor or her physician.
- Get educated on postpartum depression with information from her doctor, hospital or online.
- Talk to her about postpartum depression, about how she feels, as well as about how you feel.
- Get involved in her treatment by going with her to visit the doctor and/or her therapist.
- Call in the reinforcements: reach out to her family and friends, and call on support groups.
- Reassure her by consistently reminding her that you will be there for her, that you will get through it together, and that it will pass.

Take it seriously, take action, and you will get through it together.

> ❝ *Remember your wife has gone through a lot of changes. You'll find that she'll start crying and she won't know why. Just hold her hand and tell her it's going to be okay. She's going to be sore, tired, overwhelmed; she'll think she's ugly or a bad mom. And you're going to think you're a bad dad sometimes, too! So just be patient and keep communication open about everything.* ❞
> *- Veteran Dad*

HELP HER SUCCEED AS A MOM

Help Her Bond With Her Baby

Don't be surprised or disappointed if your mate does not mimic the stereotypical mother who falls in love with her baby at first sight. While moms tend to bond faster than dads, many experience difficulties developing a deep emotional attachment with their babies. In fact, women sometimes experience weeks of tortured insecurity and doubt about their ability to love this needy, crying, demanding and incomprehensible child.

Sometimes it only takes a sympathetic ear or even a good laugh to dispel the myths of automatic bonding and unqualified love. Let her know that her feelings are more normal than society's unrealistic expectations of her to be some kind of saint. To help her connect and develop confidence in her capabilities as a mother, point out all the things she does right for the baby. Encourage her to touch, cuddle and engage in regular skin-to skin contact with the baby.

Mothers who get a late start on bonding move on to develop as strong a relationship with their babies as those who get an early start. Moving forward is the objective, and getting overly anxious over bonding can become an obstacle along her path; so help her lighten up on herself and do the little things that help make it happen, like giving her a break.

Reassure and Encourage Her

A mom can feel incompetent or even guilty when she cannot calm her crying baby because her "maternal instinct" is supposed to tell her exactly why the baby is crying and how to comfort him. Being dead tired, feeling fat and unattractive, having little control over her own emotions, and seeing no end in sight can make her plight seem hopeless.

Encouragement and support by dad is essential. Point out what a great job she is doing, what a wonderful baby she produced, and how much you appreciate her. The more support, the better the mom. Assure her that you are in it together and you will get through it together. Be positive, constructive, and help build her confidence. Keep in mind she is in a process, and that you can't nag her into motherhood. Build her up instead.

Help Her Deal With Isolation

After a month or so, the excitement over the baby's birth winds down, the calls and visits taper off, and mom no longer attracts much attention.

- ☐ Encourage contact with other mothers (friends, neighbors, her mom, in laws, birth classmates) who can provide guidance and a strong sense of security. Others in a similar situation will serve as a readily available support system.

- ☐ Encourage her to join a new moms group where she will connect with other moms who fully understand her situation, are highly sympathetic, and have lots of ideas and advice she can trust.

- ☐ Encourage her to get out. Although babies tend to be portable, going out with a newborn can be so much work that it may not happen as often as it should.

Recognize Her "Gatekeeping" for What It Is

A mother has an intense relationship with her baby, and it's not always easy, even if she is exhausted, for her to share him with you. There you are, primed and ready to do your part, and she's hovering over you, scrutinizing everything you try to do. What do you do if your wife wants to do everything herself?

- ☐ Remind her that you need the practice. Let her know how important being close to your son or daughter is to you, right from the beginning. Stand your ground gently, and suggest she'll be glad for your involvement in the long run.
- ☐ If she's constantly looking over your shoulder and correcting you, take the baby into another room. Get out alone with your baby to prove to her that you are fully capable of taking care of your own child.
- ☐ Understand that her life is wrapped around the baby, and her "control freak" behavior is tied directly to her desire to do a good job as a mother.

Things will balance out in time if you keep pressing to be involved and do not let her push you out of your baby's life.

 I realized that I should sacrifice some of my free time to relieve my wife and encourage her to go and treat herself to lunch with a friend, a manicure, or whatever.

- Veteran Dad

4 Caring for Mom

CARING FOR A NEW MOM

Most new mothers struggle in the first few weeks, or even months. She needs to physically recover from pregnancy and childbirth, her emotions still can run rampant, she gets no more than a few hours rest at a time, and she may feel trapped or virtually chained to the baby. It can be worse, so review the information on post partum depression on page 4F and be prepared for whatever happens.

Her Expectations of Herself May Exceed Reality

A new mom will get more than tired; she can suffer from extreme fatigue. It's caused not only by the unpredictability of the baby waking to nurse every few hours, but also by the constant pressure of feeling she is responsible for her baby's survival. Exhausted and overwhelmed, she may feel she is expected to inherently know what to do with a crying infant and be as happy as a little girl playing with her favorite doll. Make sure you don't expect this, and that she knows it.

Her Maternal Instincts Will Kick In

In time her maternal instincts will kick in. It will boost her confidence, which in turn will allow her to relax. As she learns to trust her instincts and steadily develops confidence, the realization that she is a real mom will set in. She will take on the aura of one who has been tested and has proven herself, and will become a mother in her own mind. It is an awesome transformation. Your encouragement and reassurance will help her get there.

How to Support a New Mom

All new mothers are different, and the one in your life may react in ways that surprise you. Be prepared early on to support her in a big way. No advice from veteran fathers is more commonly heard or strongly held than "take care of mom; no matter what, give her all the support you can."

Basic suggestions from veteran dads for helping mom in the first few weeks include:

- Quickly learn to change diapers, burp, and calm your crying baby. Show mom she can count on you.

- Coordinate help. Obtain what you need from family, friends or neighbors, and make sure it is actually helpful.

- Help her get some sleep when the baby is sleeping and when you take him for a walk in the stroller.

- Let her know that you don't expect her to be a fairy tale mom.

- In the middle of the night when the baby is crying and both of you are dead tired, find the strength to get up and handle the baby so mom can sleep.

- Impromptu backrubs leave her feeling loved and appreciated.

- An encouraging afternoon call home when your baby is fussy and mom is frustrated can be highly appreciated.

- Take a little time each day to talk about something other than the baby, especially how mom is feeling.

She expects herself to be a great mom, because anything less would mean she is depriving her baby of something he needs. Your job is to help her do her best, and to make sure she feels good about her ability to give her baby all he needs. It can take some time before this realization sets in with her.

 It's about being there at the right time and doing the right thing. When you come home give mom a kiss first, then the baby. Start the baby's bath and give mom time to reenergize.

- Veteran Dad

HER TRANSFORMATION INTO A MOM

Millenniums of evolution and socialization have a powerful impact upon our mates when they conceive our baby. They are hard wired and biologically driven to develop an intense bond, which causes them to sacrifice a great deal as they carry, give birth and care for our child. Many of us wish we had a similar bond right out of the chute, but knowing she is giving our child a tremendous gift should outweigh any envy we feel. Our bond will come in time.

Over the initial year, motherhood will change her to her core. If you track her changes month-by-month as described in pregnancy books, you'll easily lose the forest in the trees. For what happens to her goes way beyond morning sickness and breastfeeding; she is virtually reborn as a mother who unconditionally commits herself to the well-being of our child.

This metamorphosis of a woman into a mother is one of the most remarkable of all human experiences. It warrants our deep respect, but it's easy to take for granted. The more you understand, the better you can help bring out the best in her as a mom, and as a partner. You will find that in time she does the same for you as a dad.

Our Unique Perspective: A Few Things We Have Learned

Over the years, we have witnessed many thousands of new moms, and a few things we have learned include:

- Motherhood is indeed beautiful, particularly as your wife absorbs the reality of a baby growing inside her and holds him after he is born. But it can also wreak havoc on her mind, soul and body. It also may not, so don't assume anything and tune into what is actually happening to her.
- She can experience a long, tough and tumultuous ride, a physical and emotional gauntlet of thrills, pain, fierce love, depression, exhaustion, frustration and fulfillment. Since you are along for the ride, go with the flow, share in it and help her when you can; know that you cannot fix everything.
- As with fathers, a child pushes mothers to mature into a better person, just in a much shorter timeframe.
- The girl you love is still there, and if you play your cards right, in time you will get much of her back. Plus a lot more in the form of a mom.

First Babies Can Be Tough on Moms

Some new mothers would have it no other way; being a mom just fits. But for most, it is a roller coaster ride of ups and downs. Many women's modern, fast-paced lives aren't geared toward caring for a baby who will cry, nurse, and poop at all hours. Add a mother's innate, intense focus on her baby, and you will likely have some real stress and even misery. And don't forget the hormones, which supercharge her feelings, causing exhaustion and disorienting her.

New Moms Can Be Tough on New Dads

New dads are generally way behind moms on the pregnancy learning curve, and she might have concerns that you won't be there when it counts. Her body, emotions, identity, sense of worth; her very being gets wrapped around her baby. How much energy and attention will your sweetheart have left over for you? Who is the readily available target for her mood swings and frustrations? And she may feel like she is the only one having a hard time, "he's not going to be there for me, he wants me to make all the career sacrifices, all he wants to do is have sex..." It just goes with the territory.

A Window of Opportunity for Fathers

Birth is when it gets real. Not only is this when she needs you most, but once the baby arrives your support is what she'll remember in the years ahead. Bottom line – your performance during this crucial post-birth period will form the basis for her new perspective of you as the father of her child and her partner as a parent. Given the stakes, no investment of your support and perseverance during the first several months can be too much, so dig deep.

 Having the baby in our life has added so much more, I can't even begin to tell you. We lie together in bed at night talking about our dreams for our child and how much it's brought us together.

- Veteran Dad

HER PREGNANCY BY TRIMESTER

This overview gives you the rundown on what to expect during her pregnancy by every 3 month period (trimester), so consider this the "cliff notes" to her 500 page month-by-month version (which gives her even more to worry about by covering every possible problem she or her baby can experience). Stay tuned in to what she is experiencing and look for opportunities to help her through pregnancy.

First Trimester

From the point of conception, her body begins to react even though her pregnancy is not apparent. A wide range of symptoms can accompany pregnancy; some of the physical and emotional changes that she is likely to experience in the first three months are:

✓ Nausea and vomiting	✓ Frequent urination	✓ Tiredness
✓ Breast tenderness	✓ Mood swings	✓ Odd tastes, cravings
✓ Heightened sense of smell	✓ Weight gain	

During the first trimester it is imperative for mom to take care of herself. No smoking or alcohol, good nutrition, prenatal vitamins, moderate exercise, and plenty of rest make for a healthy pregnancy. If she does not have one, she needs to find a doctor (ask around). She should make an appointment for her first prenatal visit at about eight weeks. If at any time you have concerns about your mate's condition — unusual pain, bleeding, etc. — *call her doctor.*

Prenatal care is essential as this is the most crucial time in your baby's development. This is also when he is most vulnerable to harm from alcohol, x-rays and other toxins, so help her stay informed and protected.

Second Trimester

In the next three months, some of her first trimester symptoms like nausea and fatigue tend to subside, although not entirely. They are replaced by a variety of new symptoms:

✓ Renewed energy	✓ Emotional contentment	✓ First fetal movements
✓ Headaches	✓ Heartburn	✓ Hemorrhoids
✓ Constipation	✓ Leg cramps, especially at night	✓ Swelling of legs, feet, and hands
✓ Skin, hair, and nails change	✓ Clumsiness, forgetfulness	✓ Impaired vision
✓ Faintness, dizziness	✓ Varicose veins	

Her body is definitely taking on a pregnant shape, and she'll probably need to start wearing loose or maternity clothes. She should have her energy back, and with it a sense of emotional well being. She may feel a return of libido (enjoy it while you can!). She'll be feeling the baby move now. Wait a few more weeks, and you will too.

Third Trimester

In the final three months, her previous symptoms continue and magnify:

✓ Frequent and urgent urination	✓ Hip and pelvic pains	✓ Backaches
✓ Sleeplessness	✓ Shortness of breath	✓ Impatience and frustration
✓ Braxton-Hicks (false) contractions	✓ Anxiety over delivery	✓ Disturbing dreams about baby

Although she's in the home stretch, she feels more anxious now than ever, with her energy level dropping and concerns about preparedness rising. She may waiver between feeling completely enthusiastic and completely anxious. Birth preparation classes are standard and important, not only so you'll both understand what to expect during labor and delivery, but also to ease your fears of the unknown.

As D-Day Approaches

The last few weeks are when she needs you the most, since many moms get scared of giving birth. Plan on spending most of your time with her, avoid trips away if possible, and stay in touch by phone. If she is working during this period (doctors routinely place moms on disability near the due date), she may have no desire to go and may find it difficult to focus.

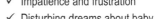 *I have also learned to have patience with my wife; she's got a lot of hormones running through her and has a lot of apprehensions too. I'm the one with the easy job of being able to kind of sit back, and she is the one who is actually pregnant.*

- *Rookie Dad*

HOW TO SUPPORT A MOM-TO-BE

By far the most prevalent advice from our veteran dads is to "take care of mom; no matter what she is experiencing, no matter how tough she is on you, take care of her." Start early in her pregnancy and here is how you do it:

Talk to Her: About the baby, her thoughts and concerns, yours too, your plans as a family, and make it a habit to ask how she is doing. Even if she seems to be handling pregnancy okay, don't underestimate its impact upon her. Just the two of you talking is the best way to prepare to be a family, and if you are a man of few words, make a list of topics so you don't run out of things to say.

Walk With Her: Pregnancy will limit her physical activity and your nightlife, but instead of just sitting around together watching TV, invite her to take walks with you. It benefits her moods, makes the birth easier and gives her a head start on getting her body back afterward. You could probably use some exercise as well, and walking and talking go hand-in-hand.

Show her that you care: Men tend to be creative, and this is a great time for thinking outside the box to show her that you care about her and the baby. If she develops a craving for ice cream, call her from the ice cream store and read her the flavors. Make a cradle for your baby if you can, or paint stars and rainbows on the ceiling in the nursery. Use your imagination.

Don't Take It Personally

Mom's hormone-driven mood swings and frustration are the norm. It's no fun, but serving as her punching bag to help exorcise her frustrations is just one of our jobs. Remind her (and yourself) of their natural cause and that they will pass. Help her get rest, time alone, and exercise. Reassure her it will all work out and she will be a great mom, count to 10, and don't get sucked into arguments.

Get Up To Speed On Her Symptoms: You will never keep up with her reading, but if you at least scan one of her favorite books, you will surprise and please her with your knowledge. And you can use it to help her cope.

Help Her Through the Pregnancy: The physical and emotional impacts of her pregnancy may be intense, and if so she will depend on you to help her get through the roughest times. It may be up to you to save her from herself as she's started on the second jar of pickles, or if she's sneaking a cigarette in the bathroom. A few ideas on how you can help; ask her for others:

☐ **Morning Sickness:** It hits most new moms, comes early in her pregnancy and can happen any time of day. While food may seem to be the problem, eating food that she can handle is the antidote. Brainstorm with her on foods she might try (nuts, fruits, vegetables) and indulge her cravings by keeping them stocked. Encourage her to eat smaller meals more frequently, to eat slowly, and stay hydrated. If she looks like she may lose her lunch, help her get to the bathroom and help her clean up.

If She Gets To Be Too Much

The antidote is *BREATHE!* by Mason Brown, from National Lampoon. It's sacrilegious and politically incorrect take on new parenthood and new moms requires that we condemn it of course, but we suggest you judge it for yourself. If you can get her to laugh with you, you will live happily ever after. Or she could respond in a less positive way.

☐ **Backache:** Weight gain, a shifting center of gravity, inactivity, inability to stretch, and a growing baby pushing her pelvic structure open all conspire to produce back problems. Due to their effect on the baby, painkillers are generally not permitted. You can help by giving her back rubs. Use the best technique you can muster by asking her how and where to rub. Help her find support straps for pregnant moms that lift her belly and a body pillow so she can swing one leg and arm over it while sleeping.

☐ **Sore Breasts:** They start growing early in pregnancy and keep growing, often causing pain and tenderness. If so, suggest a special pregnancy support bra. Offer to massage them, perhaps using her stretch mark prevention lotion; stay away from her nipples. Pour her a warm bath. Be very gentle in love making; if she asks, place her breasts "off limits" until the soreness subsides.

Go to Her Doctor Visits: This is the single most important thing you can do during pregnancy, as visits with her obstetrician get you personally connected with what's going on both with mom and your baby. Being there lets mom know she isn't alone. If you are unable to go to any visit be sure to ask her what happened. When you are with the doctor, don't be shy about asking questions. If you're being ignored, be assertive, but keep the focus on mom. Make sure she is getting all of her questions asked and answered.

> **"D**o anything you can to help your wife go through the process of being a mother. Even though it's more natural for her, it also requires an adjustment that's much greater for a woman because there are demands being put on her body that you don't experience. So the best thing to do is swallow your own point of view for awhile and just be there.**"**
>
> *- Veteran Dad*

4 Caring for Mom

Notes

Notes

STARTING A LIFE LONG LOVE AFFAIR

After a century or so of baby care being considered women's work, men collectively don't have a lot of experience with infants. So it will be a pleasant surprise when the notion that men are inherently ignorant and incapable with babies evaporates the first time you rock yours to sleep in your arms. There will be many other pleasant surprises too, like the first time she smiles at you, says "da da," and gets excited to see you. You start getting the impression that not only does this little thing like you, when it comes to the "big guy" in her life, only you will do. Even if her cries irritate you, once she falls asleep on your shoulder, snuggling into you for warmth and protection, you feel very lucky to have her.

First Wonder of Your World

Considering the billions of babies born over the millennia, it seems impossible that any one of them could be special. But yours will be. Your baby represents your own immortality, and the future of mankind, and the meaning of your life – not to mention her own unique and incredible potential as a human being. Accepting the enormity presented by your child can take you years.

Babies Can Also Be Boring, Frustrating and Irritating

Babies can be a wonderful source of happiness, but there's a flip side. It just goes with the territory, especially if you're unsure of how to care for and play with them. In any situation, there's always something that you haven't tried that may work, and the more you try, the better you will get. Your ability to maintain a positive attitude will be tied to your competence, and that comes from knowing that there is always something more that can be tried to quiet your crying baby or put your tired baby to sleep.

Courting Your Baby

The notion of courtship between a father and his baby is a good analogy, because it's a relationship that needs to develop, and this will take time. Seek out the opportunities early on to take her out with you, tell her about your world, and defend her from all threats. These actions create true love, and if the opportunities are consistently pursued, a very deep and enduring relationship is the result. The more time you spend with your baby, the better you will know her and the more she will respond to you.

Start a Lifelong Love Affair

The regular expression of love and encouragement to your child is the most important practice you can develop. We tend to be more critical of ourselves than others, and we extend this to our children, especially our firstborn. While at times negative feedback may be appropriate with her, the rule should be regular expressions that are very positive. Your child's self esteem, motivation, and zest for life to a large extent will correlate with how positive you are in her upbringing. Saying "I love you" often will also become a self fulfilling prophecy on both ends.

This practice ultimately becomes a habit, and is one that should start on day one of your child's life. With your child in your arms, look into his eyes and gently murmur how beautiful he is. When he grabs your finger, tell him how strong he is. If he burps, tell him what a good burper he is. Crying indicates healthy lungs, and potential as a singer. Crying at night indicates a partier. You get the idea – your child can do no wrong.

Nothing Like Knowing You Were There When It Counted

Tough babies, like those with colic, present a special opportunity for dads. We have no choice but to get involved with their care, but it is over at around three months and then you have decades knowing that you were there for her when she needed you. Not a bad way to start your legacy as a father.

 You get into an upward spiral - he gets to know you, you feel great - play more, he smiles more, etc. You have bad days but it always keeps getting better.

- Veteran Dad **,,**

Caring for Baby

1ST YEAR ESCAPADES FOR DADS & BABIES

Baby's Ability	Opportunities For Dad	Baby's Growth
1st Quarter	**He will be very laid back and just take it all in, so start by engaging his senses.**	**Small steps spark big growth.**
Follows things with eyes	Slowly move bright object side-to-side close to his face, and then up and down.	Visual skills, peripheral vision
Responds to sounds	Talk to her with different tones of voice and sing to her (she'll "coo" back sooner).	Sound differentiation, recognition
Intrigued by textures	Let her feel and explore your face, and things with different textures around the house.	Tactile senses, exploration
Sees at close range	Show him his face in a mirror, make faces, stick out tongue. He may imitate you.	Perception, facial expression
Lifts head when on belly	Get down nose-to-nose and talk to him; make tummy time fun, encourage mini-pushups.	Upper body and core strength
Tightly grasps things	Lie her on your lap and let her grasp your little fingers and do baby pull ups as you talk.	Arm strength and coordination
Smiles, coos, laughs	Smile and laugh back, and when he coos at you, mimic him (your response will delight him).	Verbal skills, sense of humor
Sees color and distance	Turn out lights in the nursery, turn on flashlight and shine it on colorful things in room.	Observation, inquisitiveness
2nd Quarter	**As she gets more active, engage her physically, which is a dad specialty!**	**This is where the fun starts.**
Can stand while held	Stand her on lap and hold her as she does squats, even jumps through full range of motion.	Leg strength, fast twitch muscles
Reaches for, grabs objects	Tour house with him in a front carrier and let him grab and feel safe things within his reach.	Hand-to-eye coordination
Rolls over	Put her on a blanket on the floor and encourage her to roll by placing a toy just out of reach.	Strength, flexibility, determination
Imitates sounds	Sing a lullaby, rock 'n' roll or drinking song; repetition and your enthusiasm are key.	Language skills, concentration
Moves objects hand to hand	Start him on blocks; let him bang them, build him something to knock down, help him build.	Fine muscle-control, creativity
Can put toes in her mouth	Dip her big toe in your ice cream cone and pop it in her mouth a few times.	Flexibility, surprise, delight
Inspects objects in detail	Give her interesting things and pictures of faces to inspect; point out features/names.	Ability to focus, attention span
3rd Quarter	**Now he starts to get mobile so give him room to roam and get outdoors.**	**Patience is essential.**
Sits up without support	Time to invest in a backpack baby carrier and go on hiking adventures; start with short trips.	Comfortable/fascinated outdoors
Feeds himself	Let him try with his hands and then guide his hand holding a spoon; be prepared for a mess.	Independence, coordination
Crawls, scoots or rolls	Crawlers have 4-wheel drive, so build off-road course with cushions and sheets for tunnels.	Strength, agility, motivation
Superb upper body strength	Ready to wrestle! Roll her over and back, let her grab your face, raspberries on her tummy.	Strength, trust, toughness
Jabbers away	Jabber back with delight; read her anything at all; tell her jokes; notice her jabber cadence.	Communication, personality
Learning object's names	Tell her names of things; ball, nose, toes, "da da", etc.; repeat them regularly; cheer her on.	Language formation
Walks holding onto things	Set up a track where she can fall safely; encourage exploration by putting her toys out.	Exploration, determination
Bangs and throws things	Skills dads excel at! Start a kitchen band, play retriever to his errant throws, roll ball back.	Enthusiasm for sports, music
4th Quarter	**Her skills are converging; she will hit a lot of milestones and get "active."**	**Try to keep up with her.**
Searches for hidden objects	Start with peek-a-boo and ramp up to teaching her to find toys and other treasures.	Problem solving, motivation
Will imitate you	Teach him "high five," "touchdown," etc.; develop a "secret handshake" for just the two of you.	Learning skills, socialization
Starts to say words	Your reaction to "da da" will quickly teach her to work you for all you are worth (and more).	Communication, people skills
Stands and begins to walk	She will amaze herself at first; keep her safe and eventually play "I am going to get you."	Balance, risk taking, anticipation
Put toys away (really)	Babies like to pull things out and put things into containers, so teach her to play "cleanup."	Following direction, patience
Can "draw" with a crayon	Encourage your budding artist with her choice of bold colors along with your own artistry.	Imagination, fine motor skills
Loves balls, bath & air time	Go for it; balls everywhere, toys in the tub, and airplane complete with sound effects.	How to have great fun with dad

SHOW YOUR BABY THE WORLD

Why He Picks You for Play

It starts right after birth when your bright little bundle notices that you look, smell, feel and sound different than mom. Your baby won't know what to think of you right off, which is why he stares at you so much. As the weeks go by, a baby notices mom tends to be protective and calming, while dad is more playful, physical, and often surprising. Your baby soon learns that mom will pick him up when he is fussy, but dad tends to tickle him or lift him into the air. When even a very young baby hears his father's voice he's likely to raise his shoulders and eyebrows, or begin kicking his legs, in anticipation of some excitement. Playing teaches him how to laugh and take risks. It develops his motor skills and speeds the development of his brain and nervous system. Very serious stuff, and just what dads are for.

Never underestimate the power of play. For example, the skills a three-month old baby learns by playing a simple game of "peek-a-boo!" includes, observation, language, coordination, communication, exploration, problem solving, socialization, rhythm, creativity and humor. Other games work on things like dexterity, balance, trust, strength and timing.

"For in the child lies the future of the world. Mother must hold him close so he knows it is his world. Father must take the child to the highest hill so he can see what his world is like."

Mayan Proverb

Mom and Dad: Complementary Roles For Raising Babies

While they can come into conflict, a father's adventurous role complements that of a mother's, and the combination is what turns out well rounded children. Dads introduce new challenges to their babies and encourage them to explore their worlds. Bottom line, playtime with dad contributes to your baby's physical, intellectual, and social development, and leads to great qualities later in life: good relationships with peers, a knowledge of limits, a spirit of adventure.

Show Him the World

As chief adventure officer in your new family, this is your job. Babies are incredibly curious and will become still, watchful, and even mesmerized with anything new to check out. If he is fussy, it is also distraction at its best.

Start by carrying him against your chest facing out, with one hand under his bottom and the other over his chest, with his head resting against you. Or get a front carrier and face him out. Just walk around slowly, positioning him so new things come into his field of vision. It doesn't matter what it is; just watch his face to see what captures his attention. Describe it to him in a soft voice and just let him take it in.

Around the House: Start with wallpaper and a light switch and move on to pictures, mirrors (always interesting) and windows. The kitchen is full of interesting stuff, so take your time and open the cupboards one at a time. A garden with flowers is great; let her check them out and touch them (careful she doesn't try to eat them). Bugs are very cool as they crawl around; ditto on the eating.

Away From Home: Every new place presents new opportunities; someone else's house, the neighborhood, a park, mall, or even a truck dealer. Getting fussy at a restaurant? Show him the pictures in the hall, or take a walk outside where you can introduce him to cool cars. Make sure the diaper bag is fully stocked for an outing that will last more than a few hours, and when it is nap time wrap him up in a familiar blanket from his crib and hold him so he gets warm and falls asleep.

The Hardware Store Baby Tour: It's hard to imagine a place with more interesting stuff for a baby to check out than a hardware store; aisle after aisle with lots of colors, tools and materials you can tell her about. Be careful she doesn't get close enough to grab things, but letting her get the feel of a hammer while you firmly hold the hammer's head in your hand is fine.

" *He's mesmerized by anything new. He just sucks it all in.*

- Veteran Dad

HOW YOUR BABY GROWS AND DEVELOPS

Incredible Brain Development

While the typical infant spends two-thirds of her day sleeping and the rest eating, crying, pooping and staring into space, there is also an amazing process underway inside her brain. At birth a baby's brain contains 100 billion neurons (all the nerve cells she will ever have) but the cells are not "programmed." Sensory experiences involving sight, smell, touch, etc., are what connect the neurons and "program" the brain for functions like language, vision, understanding, and physical coordination.

Just after birth, her brain produces trillions of connections between the neurons and begins the process of stimulating those that will be used and eliminating those that won't. Every stimulant helps forge a path between her brain cells, much like an electrical grid that connects neighborhoods and cities. Rich experiences produce rich brains. Like a muscle, a baby's brain increases its capability based on how much it's used.

Help Your Baby Grow

A stimulating environment doesn't mean flash cards, videos, or the many other commercial products being pushed on new parents who want to give their child the best possible start in life. What it does mean is deceptively simple: babies learn by reacting to the sights, sounds, smells and shapes around them. They also learn by meeting challenges put before them – reaching, grabbing, and getting you to pay attention. As a father, you can bring a different set of learning experiences than mom to your baby's world. Stimulate your baby by talking to her, touching her, being affectionate, showing her the world around her, and introducing objects for her to see, feel, taste, and experience.

Play with Your Baby

Start early, as having fun is the best brain developer of all. This includes letting her grasp your finger, showing your baby her reflection in a mirror, and making new sounds for her to figure out. Play improves her senses and muscle development and control, and builds her sense of inner excitement. Never underestimate the power of play. For example, the skills a three-month old baby learns by playing a simple game of "peek-a-boo!" include observation, language, coordination, communication, exploration, problem solving, socialization, creativity and humor. Other games work on physical factors like dexterity, balance, trust, strength and timing. Repetition will enhance your baby's learning new games and skills.

Talk, Sing and Read

Your voice can soothe and delight. Babies pick up inflections, gestures, and start to understand storytelling at a young age. Some will utter nonsensical sounds mimicking you. Talk to her about daily events, sports news, your job; anything at all. Sing and read as well. Use a variety of high and low pitches, loud and soft tones.

Nurture an Adventurous Spirit

Notice when he's reaching out for something and encourage his exploration. Let him take his time. Let him try for something just beyond his reach. Before you do something for him, let him try to do it himself. Encourage but don't frustrate, or you run the risk of diminishing his natural inquisitiveness and motivation. And never scare a baby; the effects will inhibit rather than nurture his adventurous spirit.

Improvise

Put your own creative stamp on playing with your baby; build your repertoire of games that only she and you know. Opportunities abound: Make your sock into a puppet and make it "sing" to him. Start to blow raspberries a couple of times on his tummy and then stop until he is bouncing with anticipation. Then cut loose with a big one. Let her splash in the bath – on you. Lay down on your back, sit him on your chest, and let him explore your face, check out how your beard feels, and grab your nose. Go roller blading while pushing him in the stroller (slowly). Let her strum your guitar.

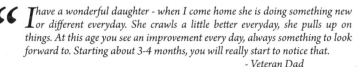

> *I have a wonderful daughter - when I come home she is doing something new or different everyday. She crawls a little better everyday, she pulls up on things. At this age you see an improvement every day, always something to look forward to. Starting about 3-4 months, you will really start to notice that.*
> *- Veteran Dad*

3 Caring for Baby

WAYS TO CALM A CRYING BABY

Need more ideas? Here are some suggestions on possible fixes:

Feeding: If it's her normal feeding schedule, hand her to mom or get the bottle. If it isn't her normal time but you think she might be hungry, go for it.

Changing diaper: Make sure you treat any redness with ointment, because a diaper rash can hurt.

Burping: Babies can swallow air while crying, so even if she hasn't eaten in a while it's worth a shot.

Infant Swing: A battery-powered infant swing is considered essential by many. Just strap your baby in and switch it on for soothing back-and-forth motion that buys you time to get things done.

Swaddling: Crying, flailing babies can be tough, but swaddling is a proven method for calming a baby and keeping him calm.

Sucking: Put your knuckle to his lips to see if he wants to suck. If he starts going at it, pop in a pacifier or use your finger, soft side up.

Bicycle Her Legs: A taut tummy or kicking legs may indicate gas pain or constipation, so put her on your lap facing you and gently work her legs up and down.

Hold, Walk and Rock: Walk around or rock him in a rocking chair. Try holding him over your shoulder, face down over your arm, or face down across your lap. This puts a little pressure on his stomach, which is often soothing.

Frontpack, Backpack or Sling: Today's baby carriers provide a great opportunity for you to care for the baby while you work around the house or take a walk.

Check out DadsAdventure.com for other dad proven techniques.

Stroller or Jogger: The vibration transmitted from the wheels traveling over the rough pavement relaxes your little one, and the fresh air helps as well. Bundle her up if it's cool outside, and make sure there is no direct sunlight hitting her face.

Bouncy Seat: Place her into the seat, propped at a 45° angle, and position it so she can see the world. It's built to gently bounce with her movements, and may have toys, music and lights to occupy your baby's developing mind.

Music: Music to a fussy baby is, well, music to her ears. Anything you like, in moderation, can work; if you like classical, great, but rock 'n' roll with heavy bass on low volume can work great as well. Or you can try one of the many CDs made for babies.

White Noise: This can be amazingly effective for calming and lulling cranky babies to sleep. Try a hair dryer, static from a radio or record. You can also put her baby-seat on top of a running dryer for both the vibration and white noise. Be careful not to leave, even for a moment, as the dryer's vibrations can walk her seat over the edge.

Distraction: Introduce a new toy, make a funny face, massage her ears, or blow on her forehead or neck. One veteran could always calm his crying son by taking him to see the family pets. Distraction is often the key to interrupting a cycle of crying.

Bath or massage: Can be done routinely before bedtime to sooth and relax her. If you get her to sleep and then need to put her to bed in her crib, use a hair dryer to warm her bedding a little so the shock of cold sheets doesn't wake her up.

Ride in the car: A classic technique used by dads when their babies are crying. The vibration and noise will put most babies to sleep within the first mile or so.

Nothing Working? When to Put Him Down in His Crib and Walk Away

Sometimes he is just on another crying jag and there isn't anything you can do to calm him. If that's the case, leave him be for a while. It might seem harsh at the time, but his crying is one way for him to get his system back in sync. Vigorous crying is physically exhausting for a baby, and several minutes of it can actually help him sleep once he does go down.

It happens to most of us who were not dealt an "easy baby." They may be fleeting, but episodes of extreme frustration due to a crying baby are exceptionally dangerous. If you feel yourself losing control, put the baby down in the safety of his crib and walk away. Never react in anger. It is incredibly easy to permanently damage an infant's brain and shaking a baby can even lead to death. Just walk away before incessant crying pushes you to that point.

"Use your imagination. Often times it's the simplest things that work. Experiment with whatever works for you as long as it doesn't hurt the baby.
- Veteran Dad"

TROUBLESHOOTER'S GUIDE TO CRYING BABIES

If there is any challenge you need to take head on, it is learning to calm your crying baby. This is the job that can really put you to the test. If you get good at turning "howling like a banshee" into "sleeping like an angel," you are gold.

Fussing Peaks at Six Weeks; Getting Over the Three Month Hump

While the amount of crying varies among babies, they tend to follow similar patterns. As newborns, they generally do not cry very much. But then their crying increases steadily for several weeks and tends to plateau at 4-6 weeks. They can carry on for weeks, and then taper back down, with crying largely over by 3 months. For serious criers, it can be a very long 3 months, but then it is largely over.

Troubleshooter's Guide to Crying Babies

It's the middle of the night. Your son just ate an hour ago and, for no apparent reason, has spent the last 20 minutes crying. Exhausted, mom is about to lose it. You have to go to work early but pretending to be asleep is not an option. What do you do?

No worries, we got this one down 18 years ago. The *Troubleshooter's Guide to Crying Babies* employs the same practical approach you'd use in solving car or computer problems. One of the most popular lessons at Boot Camp, it has proved effective for thousands of dads. It works because, just like when a car misfires, babies cry for a reason. Taking a proactive approach enables you to remain cool, rational and focused on finding a solution.

1. **Get The Basics of Comforting Your Baby**

   Most of it comes naturally, like holding, rocking, walking and singing softly. Learn from the nurses, grandma, your mate and from your own experience. Learn to distract him from what's bothering him by doing or showing him something new that re-focuses his attention.

2. **Develop a Checklist of Reasons Why Your Baby Cries**

   Starting with the most common, a typical list might include:

✓ Hungry	✓ Tired	✓ Needs burping
✓ Gas/constipated	✓ Dirty or wet diaper	✓ Diaper rash
✓ Too hot/too cold	✓ Clothes rubbing	✓ Diaper pinching skin
✓ Needs to be held	✓ Frustrated	✓ Too much noise

   Add issues unique to your baby.

3. **Develop a Routine**

   Check each reason in sequence, ruling out problems as you try solutions.

4. **Check for New Problems**

   Sometimes crying is caused by random things; his finger may be bent back in his sleeve or a hair might be wrapped around his toe. Of course, if you think your baby needs medical attention, call your doctor.

5. **Move on to New Techniques**

   Not every problem will have a single answer. Being proactive also means trying new solutions for old problems. When you've tried everything and nothing has worked it's possible your baby is now basically "tired." After 30 minutes of crying your baby has almost certainly become overtired and simply putting him to sleep is now your main goal.

   For babies with colic or if you have basic crying concerns, check out the heavy duty techniques in "Happiest Baby on the Block."

> *"There is going to be a point when you're going to run into the end of your checklist and the baby is still crying. It happens. Sometimes a baby just cries. If anything, working my way through my baby's crying has been a real test of patience for me as a father. The worst feeling is hearing your baby cry. But sometimes you also need the patience to just put the baby down and let it cry."*
> *- Veteran Dad*

HOW CAN I HELP MY BABY GO TO SLEEP?

Newborns sleep for about 16 hours a day and wake every three to four hours. Then it is time to feed and change him and give him time to explore. He will awake in the "quiet alert" phase in which he lies still and stares at things (best time for feeding). This is followed by an "active alert" phase, which is prime playtime. When he's finished playing he might let you know by looking away, arching his back or just getting cranky. He will then cry and go back to sleep and repeat the cycle.

How To Help Your Baby Go To Sleep On His Own

Trying to alter the natural schedule of a new baby to fit in with yours early on is tempting but will just lead to frustration. There are, however, constructive steps you can take to help your baby learn to go to sleep on his own. Keep in mind that every baby is different and has unique needs, both parents must buy into whatever strategy you choose, and you both must be consistent. (Same with training a puppy.)

- Swaddle your baby so he feels secure like he was in the womb and doesn't wake himself with his jerky leg and arm movements.

- Make sure he has a full meal before putting him to bed (if he drops off to sleep while feeding, dab his forehead with a wet hand cloth to rouse him.

- Burp him after his last feeding so gas pain does not wake him up. After a big burp, if mom is craving sleep, suggest she top off the tank so he might sleep longer.

- For naps during the day, keep the noise level normal and room light, and quiet with lights off during the night (use a dim light for feeding and diaper changes), so he will learn the difference between night and day.

- Put a heating pad set to low on to the sheet when you get your baby up to nurse so the bed will be warm when you return him to it.

- Try soft music or recorded sound that mimics what he heard in the womb (water flowing) or try recording his own cries.

> ### You Can't Spoil a New Baby
>
> It's impossible for about the first year. In fact, for the first few months it is essential that you respond to your baby's cries and needs so she develops a sense of security and wellbeing.
>
> Eventually she'll learn to cry for a variety of reasons (say, for your attention), but in the beginning every cry has a specific reason.

- Develop a simple bedtime routine that in addition to feeding, diaper change and nightgown, can include a bath, massage (rub a special spot, like his forehead), or song (same one every night). Put him to sleep at the same time each night in the same place. Don't rock the baby or let mom nurse him to sleep unless this is your plan for the next year.

- At six to eight weeks, you can put him in his crib when he is groggy (e.g., rubbing eyes) but still awake to start teaching him to drift off to sleep on his own and "self soothe" when he wakes up at night. A little fussing before sleeping is normal.

Try A Sleep Training Technique After A Few Months

When your baby is about two to four months, you can try the sleep training method of your choice. They include the full "cry it out" method (parents let the baby cry herself to sleep without comforting her), the modified "cry it out" method (let the baby cry, but reassure her at regular intervals with a quiet pat on the back or soothing voice), and several others. Research shows they all can work, depending upon you and your baby. For the best information, refer to babycenter.com and look up "baby sleep training."

Consistency is the Key

Parents should give the sleep training method of their choice seven to ten days to work before changing it. Remember that whatever you start doing ... if you keep doing it ... your baby will become accustomed to it ... so make sure it is something you are happy to keep doing (e.g., rocking your baby to sleep – do you want your baby to depend on this).

Periodically invite mom to quietly check on your sleeping baby together, and marvel about your angelic little bundle. If he looks a little too quiet, go ahead and make sure he is breathing (very lightly touch his chest). We all did.

> *"There are times when I talk to my son and tell him to just go to sleep. I like to think that he understands what I'm saying. If anything, I talk to him for my peace of mind. For example, when I know he's tired and he doesn't want to go to sleep, I'll say "you can sit there and cry or go to sleep while I take a shower. You decide." And after I walk over to the shower he's cool.* - Veteran Dad*"

GREAT WAYS TO BOND WITH YOUR BABY

The bonding thing, whether it hits you at birth or sneaks up on you down the road, is unlike anything you've ever experienced, and it doesn't ever go away. In fact, it's what drives you to do your best as a father and makes all your sacrifices more than worthwhile. Here are some proven moves that will strengthen your bond with your new baby:

- ☐ **Use Your Finger as a Pacifier:** Babies love to suck. A clean finger works just as well as a pacifier, and it is a surreal feeling as you actually feel instinct at work. You can also get an idea of what it is like when he latches on to mom's breast.

- ☐ **Swaddle/Cuddle:** She makes a very huggable bundle when swaddled, wrapped in a blanket after a bath, or really just about any time. Hold her close to keep her warm, and give her the secure feeling that you'll always protect her.

- ☐ **Try Kangaroo Care:** Research found that when mothers held their premature babies to their bare chests (called Kangaroo care), both of their stress levels dropped dramatically. It also works with fathers and full-term babies, and you will find that taking off your shirt and putting your soft, freshly bathed baby on your chest is pretty close to heaven.

- ☐ **Give Him a Bath:** Research has also found that one of the best bonding strategies for dads is giving your baby a bath. If you do it regularly, it gets very interactive, and when at several months you can take him into the bath with you, it is a blast. Have mom hand him to you in the shower; socks on your hands will prevent slips and also work as wash cloths.

- ☐ **Carry Her in a Pouch:** Many dads report that carrying her in a soft front carrier is a great way to go. She can either snuggle in and fall asleep or look out at all of the new wonders of the world that continually pass by.

He Will Develop Amazing Upper Body Strength

At one day old, a baby can almost do a pull up when he grabs onto your pinkies. At several weeks he will start lifting his head, which is half his body weight, and at a few months he can rip out a fistful of your chest hair.

She Can Deeply Relax You

You get home late, stressed out after a bad day at work. The baby is fussy and mom's had it. Life sucks, right? No, because on this night, after walking with your baby, she falls asleep on your chest, a warm little bundle sleeping like an angel. Life doesn't get any better than this.

Also see the *10 Adventures* section on page 8-C.

Also see the *10 Adventures* section on page 8-C.

- ☐ **Take Her to See Your Friends:** You can stay cooped up at home, or you can go visit your friends. Park your baby in the stroller near the basketball court and shoot some hoops with the guys. You will periodically interrupt your game to check on her, but your friends will be happy to help. And by taking your baby, you are scoring points all around.

- ☐ **Talk or Sing to Your Baby:** Tell him about your day, or what he might be when he grows up. He will find everything you have to say fascinating, and when he starts babbling back, you'll be buds for life. If you sing, she will think you're the greatest. Slow tunes and lullabies are best around bedtime, but most anything you like works well for fuss prevention.

- ☐ **Get in On the Feeding:** After three to four weeks of breastfeeding, encourage mom to use a breast pump so you can feed your baby with a bottle. Mom won't be tied to the baby, and it'll give her a chance to get several hours away from home and you an opportunity to really connect.

Just the Two of You

Spending time alone with your baby is the best way to build your bond and your confidence, and a great way to make the most of being a dad. So start by spending some time alone with the baby on the day he's born; encourage mom to get out alone after you bring your baby home; and when he's ready, take him out to see the world on your own where no one else in the world can intrude. Go for a long walk, take her to the park or to your favorite surfing spot. Mom will also appreciate the balance this brings to her life, and it will help strengthen your relationship with her.

> ❝ *A man should take every opportunity to be a part of the nighttime experience. The nighttime is a magical time. Until you've sat up with your child at night while the child nurses and comes in and out of sleep, you're missing something. Not to mention that your wife could use the help. You've got the rest of your life to sleep.* ❞
> *- Veteran Dad*

3 Caring for Baby

MILESTONES FOR NEW DADS

This is not your father's fatherhood. Today, the expectations for a dad are much higher, but this also provides more opportunity for your baby to be an important part of your life.

If you like to set goals in order to measure accomplishments, then start with these seven milestones for your first three months as a father. If you're an overachiever, you can always speed up the timetable or add more milestones:

- Get hands-on experience with your baby from the very beginning at the birth and throughout the hospital stay.
- Learn the basics of holding, changing, dressing, burping, and swaddling within one week.
- Learn to comfort your crying baby within two weeks. If he has colic, try not to get too frustrated and make it four weeks.
- Select one activity – like bathing your baby or giving her "tummy time" to build upper-body strength – and make it your own within four weeks.
- When he's 6 weeks start going out with your baby, just the two of you; walks, stroller rides, etc. Get out at least once a week.
- Spend four hours alone with your baby by the end of the second month (you may have to boot mom out of the house).
- Take her on your first "show her the world" adventure – like to a hardware store – by 3 months.

By hitting these milestones you'll become an expert on taking care of your own baby. After just a few weeks of burping, swaddling, bathing, etc., taking care of him will be second nature. Your baby will also learn how dad does things. With you and him in sync nobody in the whole world, with the possible exception of mom, will do it better.

Get To Know Your Baby

All babies are unique, and understanding your child's different characteristics will help you determine your best approach to being his dad. Characteristics include how he responds to you, a wet diaper, or hunger, and how he likes to be soothed and play. Some babies thrive on interaction, while others seem more self-contained. Some babies relax and fall asleep when you gently massage them, others become rigid and seem to be uncomfortable with a lot of touching. Noticing these responses and tuning into your child enables you to respond to his individuality and efforts to learn and explore his world.

Understanding His Emerging Personality

At 4 months your baby's temperament, the technical term for his personality or nature, is emerging sufficiently to take your understanding to the next level. Caveats from the experts include that babies continually change as they grow and what you see now is not necessarily what you'll get down the road. A beautifully behaved baby may turn into a high maintenance child, or your screamer at 3 months may be mellow at 6. Focus on his current nature, try to keep up with his changes, and stay intrigued about what the future will bring. Resources to help include:

- BabyCenter.com offers their *Temperament Quiz: Rate Your Baby and Yourself*, which provides a great framework for understanding your baby and advice on how best to deal with you and your baby's specific characteristics.

- The Preventive Ounce (PreventiveOz.org) offers a survey tool that enables you to profile your baby beginning at 4 months and predict future behavior based on an extensive data base of the experiences of other parents.

Getting a handle on your child's temperament/personality will help guide your care strategies and interactions, as well as strengthen your sense of confidence as a capable parent.

> **❝** *It wasn't long before the baby began to display an individual will; a like and dislike for certain things. This began as a very small infant. These likes and dislikes don't always parallel mine. I am learning that give and take is important, even with little ones.*
> - Veteran Dad **❞**

LEARNING TO CARE FOR YOUR NEW BABY

A Little Education And Some On-The-Job Training, And You Will Become An Expert

We learn best by doing, but a little instruction goes a long way. Try the following:

☐ Learn the techniques below from the nurses in the hospital before you go home.

☐ Take a class on new baby care. Doing this with your partner allows you to learn as a team.

☐ Learn from real experts – new fathers of twins – on the *Crash Course For New Dads* DVD. Watch it with your wife, and she'll see that men are capable of caring for an infant.

☐ Check out baby care websites, like babycenter.com; baby.com; ivillage.com; aap.org; americanbaby.com.

Quick Guide to Brand New Infant Care

This is what you need to know to get started immediately with your baby:

Diaper Changes

1. Put diaper, wipes, cream, clothes, etc., within reach; lay baby on changing pad on a secure surface and keep one hand on him at all times.
2. Talk to him to distract him and minimize any fussing.
3. Undo the diaper; if a boy, place a clean diaper over his tummy and penis to avoid getting peed on.
4. If poopy, grab baby's ankles and lift over his chest and use top of old diaper to wipe away as much as you can and then tuck it under him.
5. Use wipes to thoroughly clean remaining poop.
6. Use diaper cream so the meconium in his first few stools doesn't stick to his bottom like tar. Use it on any rash that develops as well.
7. Put a new diaper under his bottom, fasten it snuggly and fold top down below his umbilical cord stump.
8. Put the used wipes in the dirty diaper and roll it up, re-applying the old tape to keep it closed.
9. Wash your hands or use a hand sanitizer.

Cord Care

Umbilical cord stumps need to be kept clean and dry before they fall off in one to three weeks. Use a Q-tip with rubbing alcohol to clean it two to three times a day while changing diapers.

Bathing

1. For the first weeks, give him a sponge bath to avoid getting his cord stump wet.
2. Put warm water in a bowl, have some mild soap handy, undress him and place him on a towel.
3. Get a soft cloth wet, add a little soap and wipe him down gently starting with his head to his toes. Be thorough on his bottom and any skin creases.
4. Rinse him using another cloth with clean water, dry him off and dress him in a clean outfit.

Feeding (with a bottle); See Helping Mom Breastfeed

1. Sit the baby on your lap and recline her slightly so that she is cradled in one of your arms.
2. Support her head and place the nipple in her mouth.
3. She may not be hungry for the first few days; to help trigger a sucking reflex, rub nipple gently on her lips or the roof of her mouth.
4. If she gags on the formula, pull nipple back a little.
5. Let her eat until she's finished.

Burping After Feeding

• While in a slightly reclined sitting position, take the baby and, while supporting his head, lay him on you chest-to-chest. Use a burp cloth – he may spit up.

• Support the baby with one arm (under his butt) while gently but firmly patting his back with your free hand.

• If nothing happens after a few minutes change his position up over your shoulder and try again.

• If nothing happens, he likely does not need to burp.

Swaddling

• Spread a receiving blanket on a flat surface.

• Place her diagonally on the blanket with her head on one corner.

• With one hand, bring the bottom corner up to her chin so her legs are tucked in.

• With the other hand, pull a side corner snuggly over her and tuck it between her back and the blanket.

• Pull the other corner over her and tuck it in.

Massaging

To relax your baby and get him to sleep longer, massage him by stroking him lightly in smooth, circular motions on the head, arms, stomach and legs. You can do it over his clothes or you can use a little baby oil on his skin.

3 Caring for Baby

> " *One time my wife left me with our baby, Madison, so she could run some errands. After my wife left, Madison wouldn't stop crying. I panicked and decided to call my wife. Just before I punched in the last number I decided NO, I'm not going to call her. I hung up the phone and started finding ways to calm Madison down. A half-hour later she finally calmed down. It proved to be a real confidence builder for me.* "
> - Veteran Dad

Notes

Notes

HOW TO GET OUT OF THE HOUSE

Basic sanity requires that you leave the confines of your house as soon as possible. This will include taking your baby out alone or with mom, taking your wife out on a date alone, and even you getting some time off for good behavior. Even sheer exhaustion in the first weeks should not preclude this as it is the antidote to the parental stress that develops early on from feeling trapped, closed-in and housebound with an incessantly demanding infant.

Dads need to take the initiative because a new mom is generally just trying to get through the day and may not get out of her bathrobe for two weeks. Don't wait six weeks for his immune system to charge up; just don't go where he will be around other people. Getting out also overcomes the "stuck at home with the baby" inertia that can otherwise set in for years, and sets in motion an active, outgoing family lifestyle.

Progressive Outings

- Pack her in the stroller and take a walk around the block. This works well with crying babies as nobody is bothered and the rumbling ride of the stroller is soothing to her. You may add a side-to-side rocking motion to enhance the effect, or cover the stroller opening with a blanket to turn out the lights (or keep the sun off her face).
- Place her in the soft front carrier facing you and go for a walk or even a short hike. The warmth of your body and walking motion will calm her and lull her to sleep; you get some exercise and relaxation as well. Since she is so close, you can talk or sing to her softly.
- You already put her in the car, strapped in according to specs, for the ride home, so the next step is to develop a proficient routine because you will be doing this a lot. Pack the diaper bag, the stroller, front carrier or later a backpack carrier so you are fully prepared for the adventures ahead.
- Make it a habit. Take her with you regularly, and figure out how to keep to her sleep schedule while out and about. She will remind you of her feeding schedule; just bring the milk, bottle and a portable bottle warmer.

Put Your Baby to Sleep Anywhere

Maintaining your baby's sleep routine does not mean it must occur in her crib. The schedule is the key, and the stroller, front carrier, and car seat all can work. If eating out during her normal nap time, place her in her seat under the table and rock it with your foot. If you go to a park, a small portable bed can work; try replicating her normal sleeping environment, wrap her up in a familiar blanket from her crib and hold her so she gets warm and falls asleep, or walk her in a stroller. Be creative; there is always a solution.

Take Your Baby Out to Eat

Restaurants and fussy babies don't mix, but you can eat out in peace:
- Work around her fussy times; try breakfast when she is rested.
- When waiting for dinner (to prevent fussiness) walk her around and show her pictures in the hall, etc.
- If she gets fussy, wrap her in a blanket and take a walk outside to calm her, or park her next to you in her stroller and rock it side-to-side.
- If it is just not going to work, ask to have your food boxed to go and try again another day.

Challenges You May Face in Getting Out Alone with Your Baby

Fear. The thought of taking your infant out on your own can be unnerving – until you do it once. Mom may not quite trust you at first, but after a few trips when you bring your baby home safe and sound (no need to report minor problems), there is little she will appreciate more than her time alone and knowing her baby has a great dad.

“The only advice I have to give is to be patient and carry an extra shirt with you wherever you go.

- Veteran Dad

STRATEGIES FOR THRIVING IN THE FIRST WEEKS

Don't Miss This Opportunity to Bond as a New Family

Having family help out can be great when you and mom are exhausted, but the first few weeks with a new baby are also a time for a new dad, mom and baby to get to know each other. Spend time alone, just the three of you. You and mom will get to know the baby's habits and routines, and you'll feel comfortable as parents quicker.

Take Great Care of Mom

This is the first piece of advice new fathers tell dads-to-be. Their specific advice includes:

- Tell her what a great mother she is. Reassure her about any concerns she has. Tell her you love her.
- Protect her from intrusive visitors, help her maximize her sleep, and make sure she eats well with regular meals.
- Understand her "ownership" issues regarding the baby. Be patient.
- Help her get a daily bath or shower, out of her robe, and some exercise.
- Get her time on her own to read, take a bath or listen to music.
- Get her more time out of the house so she can take a walk, visit a friend, go to an exercise class, or just breathe.
- Make sure she gets appropriate health care and help her with any "baby blues" or depression issues. (See page 4-F).
- Encourage her to join and regularly participate in a local mothers group so she does not feel isolated.

Additional tips can be found in *How To Support A Mom-To-Be* on page 4-A.

Your Attitude Counts Big

In the first weeks after the birth, new moms often find themselves on an emotional roller coaster with feelings ranging from deep happiness to inadequacy and frustration. Dads are usually along for the ride. As time wears on, new moms and dads wear down, and start asking "will it ever end?" It's a prescription for turning "starting a family" into a depressing experience.

When the chips are down, attitude means everything, and with mom focused on the baby, this mostly means your attitude. We'll spare you the platitudes (e.g., suck it up) because you won't want to hear them, but just know that this is your trial by fire on your path to fatherhood. Consider the following to help maintain your attitude:

- Boost or reactivate your's and mom's sense of humor by stocking up on DVDs of comedies and comedians.
- Get together with other new parents; sharing experiences is very therapeutic as there is always someone worse off.
- Take care of yourself in terms of health, and get some time alone with your buddies on occasion.
- If things get real tough, knowing that you were there when your child really needed you will last your lifetime.

Romance and Fun

Well, not much romance at first, but it is never too early to start warming her back up. Getting out and making her laugh is a great way to start. Newborns sleep for hours and can be quiet enough to allow you to go to a restaurant or movie. Just getting out together to take the baby for a walk in the stroller can invigorate your bond. See *Romancing A New Mom* on page 4-G.

Make Your Fatherhood Your Own

As a new dad today, you have unprecedented opportunities to be part of your child's life. You also have forces pushing you away, such as your career commitments, your current life that you know and love, or perhaps mom's gate keeping or the example set by your own father. You have serious choices to make.

The counter force comes from your child, who is designed to compete effectively for your heart. The trick for you is to trust yourself with your baby, spend time together away from mom, and follow your instincts. Dads tend to be creative problem solvers, so if he is fussy, come up with your own solution like holding him and bouncing on an exercise ball. Buy matching hats. Teach him a secret handshake. While I know no one who has tried, if you learn to put him to sleep by safely mounting his car seat on an idling large block Chevy V8 engine (the low rumble mimics a mother's heartbeat), you will be a legend among dads, and you will have definitively made your fatherhood your own.

> " *My best move as a dad was getting involved with the baby from the beginning, including feeding, bathing, and changing diapers. It built a strong foundation for the relationship with my child and helped strengthen the relationship with my wife.*
> - Veteran Dad "

SUPPORT & EMERGENCY CONTACTS

Emergency number **911**	Poison Center: **(800) 222-1222**
Hospital emergency room	Nurse answer line
Baby's pediatrician	Mom's obstetrician
Lactation consultant	
Friend	Friend
Relative	Relative
Dad Contact	Mom Contact
Nanny or day care center	Alarm Company
Plumber	Veterinarian
Dentist	Take-out restaurant
Other	

Child's Information

First Name:	Last Name:
Date of Birth:	
Weight:	as of (date):
Medical Conditions:	Allergies:
Health Insurance:	Policy/Group #:

2 Settling In

WEEKLY SURVIVAL CHART* (Plan Your Support/Tasks)

	Sunday	Monday	Tuesday	Wednesday	Thursday	Friday	Saturday
Morning	BREAKFAST						
	SUPPORT						
	TO DO						
Afternoon	LUNCH						
	SUPPORT						
	TO DO						
Night	DINNER						
	SUPPORT						
	TO DO						

*Note who brings dinner, when basic household tasks are to be done, doctor visits, who is coming to help, etc. A plan makes it less overwhelming.

WEEKLY SURVIVAL CHART* (Plan Your Support/Tasks)

	Sunday	Monday	Tuesday	Wednesday	Thursday	Friday	Saturday
Morning		BREAKFAST					
		SUPPORT					
		TO DO					
Afternoon		LUNCH					
		SUPPORT					
		TO DO					
Night		DINNER					
		SUPPORT					
		TO DO					

*Note who brings dinner, when basic household tasks are to be done, doctor visits, who is coming to help, etc. A plan makes it less overwhelming.

2 Settling In

WEEKLY SURVIVAL CHART* (Plan Your Support/Tasks)

	Sunday	Monday	Tuesday	Wednesday	Thursday	Friday	Saturday
Morning	BREAKFAST						
	SUPPORT						
	TO DO						
Afternoon	LUNCH						
	SUPPORT						
	TO DO						
Night	DINNER						
	SUPPORT						
	TO DO						

*Note who brings dinner, when basic household tasks are to be done, doctor visits, who is coming to help, etc. A plan makes it less overwhelming.

MAKE THE MOST OF YOUR FIRST DAY AS A FATHER

Your baby is brand new, your wife is now a new mom, and you are a new father. This is a very special time for you to get to know each other and bond as a family, so relish the moments by just being together, alone. Don't let work or other issues intrude on your first days, and take advantage of the opportunity to care for your baby.

Learn From the Nurses

OB nurses are experts on newborns and are usually happy to teach you basic skills on comforting, changing, bathing and swaddling your baby. They love babies and will be very pleased to know "their baby" has a father who wants to take great care of him. Don't be shy about asking the nurse to show you how, and take advantage of any opportunity to learn.

Take Care of Mom

Help mom deal with her medical issues, breastfeeding, etc., so you won't be clueless when you get home. Tell her what a great mom she is and how much you love her. Don't let mom feel compelled to have the baby in the room all the time. If she needs a break, ask the nurse if the baby can go to the nursery for a while.

Manage Your Visitors

A few low key visits are cool, and give you a chance to show off the baby, but don't feel pressured to have a lot of visits. The best excuse for limiting visits is: "she is exhausted and needs to sleep," which is generally the case anyway, and visitors can always come by the house later to see the baby. Make sure all visitors wash their hands before handling the baby, as his immune system is underdeveloped. Wash yours, too.

Change Your Baby's First Diaper

One veteran dad reported that he made it a point to change his baby's first diaper so he "could set the tone" that he was serious about taking care of his child. Then he showed his wife how, which built her confidence in him.

Start Falling in Love

"Bonding" is falling in love with your baby. You might fall head over heals the moment you see him. Many dads, however, report feeling disconnected from their child even months after the birth, so if you don't feel "bonded" to your baby at first, don't worry. Becoming a father is a process and you can't rush it. Just take advantage of the opportunities you have to be with him. Hold him in your arms and look in his eyes, check out his fingers and toes, snuggle her to your chest until she falls asleep and feels like she is part of you. If you're feeling uncomfortable, the last thing you want to do is shy away from him. Just give it time; trust that it will happen.

Before You Leave the Hospital

- Announce the news - get out the address book and call.
- Get more pictures - you can never take too many - and get in the picture yourself.
- Make sure your home is ready; ask for help in cleaning, setting the thermostat, stocking it with baby supplies, etc.
- Make sure the car is good to go with an installed baby seat.

Congratulations, Dad!

It might take time to accept the full magnitude of what you have done, but you're now a father and you will be forever. Try and take a moment to recognize that you are now a dad who is doing a job for his family. If this notion doesn't fully register, carry your baby into the bathroom and look at yourself in the mirror. Tell yourself "nice job, dad," and take pride in the fact that you have what it takes.

Welcome to Fatherhood! Try and get some sleep; you're going to need it.

> *When it's your turn, make it you and her. Just ignore everybody else or anything else going on. Grab your baby's hands, grab her toes, smooth her head, just touch her, squeeze her just slightly. Look at her, talk to her, knowing that you're doing her good, and she'll like it. This is the best way to get a good start.*
> *- Veteran Dad*

HELPING MOM BREASTFEED

The broad benefits of breastfeeding have been firmly established by research and a record proportion of mothers (about 75%) are giving it their best shot. Despite a broad assumption that breastfeeding is the most natural (next to birth) thing for a mother to do, many run into problems and quit early. Being natural and being easy are two completely different things, and this means dad has a major support role in helping mom and baby get breastfeeding down.

Common Problems

There are a lot of things that can create problems for your little one when he's trying to eat in those first days:

*   **Latching on:** The most common problem for a newborn is latching on properly. There are a variety of positions that can be tried (ask the nurse while you're still in the hospital) to help him get on and stay on.
*   **Nothing coming:** For the first few days after the baby is born, mom will only be producing colostrum (a nutritive rich liquid that boosts his immune system) and you might worry he's not eating enough. Almost every baby loses weight in the first few days, and once mom's milk comes in the weight will come right back.
*   **Pulling off:** Maybe she can latch on, but after just a couple of minutes she pulls off. This gets better in time as she slowly learns to coordinate sucking, drinking, and breathing.

It takes most babies a few weeks to get breastfeeding down completely. By the third week just about every baby can breastfeed with no trouble, and those early problems will largely be a part of the past.

If It Just Won't Work

Given all the benefits, it is tough for moms to stop breastfeeding even when it is obvious it is not going to work. Your job is to reassure her of your love and respect, and be the first to tell her it's no big deal. New mothers tend to beat themselves up over their inability to breastfeed, and your partner will need your support now more than ever. Even if you are disappointed that your baby will not be breast fed, the bottom line is helping your mate overcome her disappointment and get on with becoming the best mom possible to your child.

How Dad Can Help

If mom and baby are having a particularly difficult time with breastfeeding there are things you can do to help:

*   **Back rubs:** Before mom starts feeding give her a quick back rub to loosen her muscles and calm her mind. If she's in a relaxed state she'll be in a better state to deal with frustration if the baby isn't cooperating.
*   **Breast massage:** Lightly rubbing mom's breast while she's feeding stimulates milk flow and will help ensure the baby gets a good feeding.
*   **Burp the baby:** Before mom switches breasts, take the baby and burp him. This will give mom a short break, and allows you to be a part of the feeding.
*   **Calm the baby:** If she's having a hard time feeding and is getting upset, take the baby and calm her down, that way both mom and baby get a little down time before trying again.
*   **After three weeks, pitch in:** Suggest that mom pump her breast milk so you can get in on the feeding and she can get a break.

Get More Help If Needed

Most hospitals offer lactation classes or you can often have a lactation nurse visit while you're still in the hospital, and you should take full advantage. She can face more serious problems, such as medications that preclude breastfeeding, inadequate milk production, poor letdown, inverted nipples that a baby can't latch on to, or finding breastfeeding to be too painful, or demanding, especially if they feel pressure to return to work quickly. If so, suggest she talk with the lactation consultant to be sure she is aware of all alternatives. Mom's use of a breast milk pump may work, in which case your baby get's breast milk and you can get in on the feeding.

> **“** *My husband got our son onto my breast initially by dripping some sterile water onto my breast. He was so proud that it worked and that he thought of it and not me, an OB nurse. I was proud of him, too and our son was delighted.*
>
> *- Veteran Mom* **”**

GETTING SETTLED AT HOME

The exciting, exhausting 24/7 days of parenting a newborn really kick in as you drive away from the supportive embrace of the hospital. With your wife and infant in the back seat, you head off into an adventure that will require the supply lines, equipment, logistics, communications and support troops of a small military operation. It may as well be a covert gig as you will be going under deep cover and won't resurface for two to three months.

Arrange Your Family's Support System

Arrange for help from family and friends, and professionals (e.g., visiting nurse) if needed. It's a good idea to keep a list handy with phone numbers and other contact information. (See page 2-E). Don't expect your wife to handle arrangements like she usually does; she will be focused on the baby. If she had a C-section, plan on handling everything for two weeks.

Make a list of who you and mom want to ask for help, and then ask. Don't be shy about saying no to offers from those who will add rather than relieve stress. If you have family nearby, your baby will be the focus of attention for the first few weeks, so put them to work. Out-of-town relatives do not need to stay with you 24/7. Consider a hotel or a relative's home.

Keep Help Helpful

The right help makes a huge difference. Some "help" can be intrusive; working out a policy can keep everyone happy and involved:

- **Set up a schedule.** Use a calendar page (or See page 2-F) to schedule help, visitors, meal deliveries, healthcare visits for at least the first two weeks.
- **Assign tasks.** Post a "to do" list on a dry-erase board where you can note what needs to be done, so no one has to ask.
- **Dad is not third string.** Grandma is there to help, not hog the baby. Deal with it by asking her to show you what she knows about babies.
- **How long will they stay?** Even just a few days will be appreciated by you and mom, but too much can be a problem.
- **Stay flexible.** You may not need as much help as you planned on, or may need more due to post partum depression, colicky baby, etc.
- **Help means helping.** No drama, criticisms of mom, competition for the baby, etc., allowed. No issues other than making mom's life easier.
- **Hire some help.** If you can afford it, borrow a friend's cleaning lady, get a baby sitter, bring in a doula, etc.

Visitation Ground Rules

Try and balance out the desire of loved ones to see your baby (and mom's desire to show him off) with the needs of your new family. Talk with your wife and set some ground rules for visitors:

1. No unannounced or marathon visits.
2. No waking up the baby.
3. Mom is not allowed to take care of guests.
4. Visitors must wash hands before touching the baby.
5. The baby is not to be handled too much.
6. No sick visitors, especially children.
7. No unsolicited opinions on breastfeeding or anything mom does.
8. Diapers/meals are the price of admission.
9. Help with housework is encouraged.

Enforcing the rules is dad's job. (Some guys have to tell their mother-in-law, or even their own mother, to back off.)

Voicemail: Your First Line of Defense

Minimize intrusions on your new family by recording a message announcing the baby's name, weight and height, and date/time of birth, and let them know you will get back to them when you can. Turn mom's cell phone off when she is napping; same with yours.

Get Organized/Get Efficient

The trick is to settle into a manageable routine that you can maintain once the help leaves. To make it easier:
- Set up a breastfeeding station with a rocker/glider, light reading material, TV/DVD remotes and phone (with head set).
- Stock up on quick meals, take your friends up on offers to bring meals, use online grocery shopping and home delivery of restaurant meals; make large amounts of nutritious and easy soups and stews and freeze the extra in zip lock bags.
- Use paper plates and plastic utensils for two weeks.
- Keep a diaper bag well stocked with baby items to facilitate fast getaways when the need or opportunity arises.
- Rather than sleepers with lots of snaps, dress your baby in gowns to make night changes easier.
- Put mini-changing station(s) with diapers, wipes, lotion and a toy in a basket in strategic locations around the house.
- Ramp up your home entertainment system with money saved staying home, and arrange access to music, movies, etc.
- Get creative and devise your own solutions to issues that emerge during the first two to three weeks of trial and error.

> **"** *B oth my mother and mother-in-law came at the same time and my wife was getting frustrated because both mothers were telling her "no, that's not how you do that; do it this way." I had to tell the mothers that this was our daughter and we would appreciate it if they kept their comments to themselves. It is alright now, but we learned that grandmothers can just go crazy.* **"**
> *- Veteran Dad*

STRATEGIES FOR SURVIVING THE FIRST WEEKS

Make Sleep a Priority

Fatigue is typically the first and toughest challenge faced by new parents, especially nursing moms. Babies start with six to eight sleep/awake cycles per day compared to our one. If you have been exhausted before, you probably haven't experienced it like this. Sleep deprivation can cause one to become irritable and even disoriented and a vicious cycle can develop in which you cannot relax and go to sleep even when you have time. Make sleep a priority when you arrive home:

- Provide opportunities for your partner to sleep several hours during the day by taking full charge of the baby between certain breastfeedings. If necessary, insist she do so; many new mothers feel compelled to do more than they need to.
- Trade shifts with mom so you can sleep. Grab a nap when your baby is sleeping on your watch; put him on your chest where he will make sure you remember that you are on first call.
- Stock up on sleep when relatives are around to take shifts, or arrange a babysitter for several hours.
- Work out an arrangement for night in which you can share the load most efficiently (i.e., you both don't need to get up every time the baby wakes up). Talk to other parents about ideas and try out your own; e.g., a co-sleeper can make night breast feedings much easier on mom as she doesn't have to fully wake up, making it easier to get back to sleep.
- Start out building good baby sleep habits (see *How Can I Help My Baby Go To Sleep* on page 3-D), and don't get hung up with the debate over letting babies cry it out – there is a pragmatic middle ground to choose as well.

Form a Parenting Team

Nothing is more important than you and your mate working together. Learn to take care of your baby together at first, and then take shifts to give each other a break and make the best use of your time. If mom insists on doing it all, suggest she back off for her own good. Stick together no matter what. Building a family is a profound responsibility for you two.

Blow off Non-Essential Tasks

Minimize outside work responsibilities so you can concentrate on your new family. Prioritize essential tasks and focus on the basics:

- Feeding, changing and caring for your newborn.
- Eating, sleeping and showering yourselves.
- Getting to know your baby; he'll be a newborn for only a few short weeks.

Make sure any dishes are washed and the trash taken out so clutter does not add to the stress. If you cannot assign tasks to help, cut back on routine ones like cooking, laundry, shopping, vacuuming, and errand-running during the first weeks. You can catch up later. Set aside everything else like thank-you notes.

Lighten up on your expectations and encourage mom to do the same. During these initial weeks, perfectionism regarding housework is a vice, not a virtue. Be flexible and go with the flow, and after a week or so, your new life with a baby will start settling into a regular routine.

Get a Grip on Colic

For healthy babies, colic presents new parents' worst scenario. Incessant crying, less sleep, anger at your baby, feelings of failure, antagonism between mom and dad can combine to make your lives miserable for three months. You need to get ahead of the curve by becoming the expert on the aggressive crying mitigation techniques found in *Troubleshooter's Guide To Crying Babies* page 3-E, on DadsAdventure.com and in *The Happiest Baby on the Block* video.

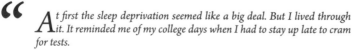

> **"** *A t first the sleep deprivation seemed like a big deal. But I lived through it. It reminded me of my college days when I had to stay up late to cram for tests.* **"**
>
> *- Veteran Dad*

Notes

Notes

HANDLING AN EMERGENCY BIRTH

The chances of having to deal with an emergency birth are extremely small, but it's normal to think about the possibility and knowing what to do can provide some reassurance. Do not attempt this unless absolutely necessary otherwise it would be an unnecessary risk to mom and baby.

When It's Too Late: If you can see the baby's head (or other part) at the vaginal opening, your mate says she can feel the baby coming, or she can't stop pushing.

1. **Call 911:** If you're at home, don't attempt to get her into a car and to the hospital. If you're home alone, call someone to assist and call her doctor. If you're in the car make sure you know how to tell the paramedics where you are – with an address or cross streets. Pull over, put on your flashers. Keep 911 on the line for instructions.

2. **Grab a Blanket:** Blankets, clothing, towels, your shirt – something you can wrap the baby in once he is born. Grab two in case you need them.

3. **Calm Mom and Slow Things Down:** Reassure her, tell her that everything's fine. Help her breathe through the contractions instead of pushing.

4. **Get Mom in Position:** Get your wife into a comfortable position lying down, instead of standing or squatting. Babies come out fast and they are slippery, making them hard to catch. Put something soft under mom's bottom where the baby may land.

5. **Get Positioned to Catch Your Baby:** Get into a position to catch her. As your baby is being born, try to get your partner to stop pushing and to just breathe. As the head appears, let it come out on its own; do not pull.

6. **Check the Umbilical Cord:** If the cord is around your baby's neck, carefully slide it over her head.

7. **Clear Your Baby's Airway:** After the cord is handled, make sure the baby's nose and mouth are clear of mucous or any other material that might impede breathing.

8. **Time For The Rest of Him:** Encourage mom to start pushing and let him slide out, putting one hand under his head and back and use the other to firmly grasp his feet as he is slippery.

9. **He Should Start Crying:** Babies usually start crying and breathing within a few seconds of being born. If he doesn't, rub his back or chest briskly or slap the soles of his feet. If that does not get him breathing, ask for instructions from 911 personnel.

10. **Don't Worry About Cutting the Cord:** It won't hurt anything to leave it until the paramedics arrive or you can get to a hospital. Same with the placenta.

11. **Place Your Baby on Mom:** Wipe the baby off quickly and place her on your partner's abdomen either on the baby's stomach or side. Then cover the baby but make sure you can see her face. Keep both your baby and mom warm.

12. **Start the Baby Nursing:** If the cord will reach, place the baby at your partner's breast and let her start suckling or nuzzling. This will help reassure mom her baby is fine.

13. **Wait for the Paramedics:** If they aren't available, carefully drive your family to the hospital's emergency entrance. Do not get excited and rush.

> " *Feeling helpless is one of my worst fears. Not knowing what to do when something unexpected happens.*
> - *Rookie Dad*

WHAT YOU NEED FOR THE HOSPITAL

Get a list together of the items you need for your hospital bag and make sure mom's and your baby's bags include the basics. Keep the list with your bag to double check before you head out (if you have time). You can get ideas from the hospital staff and birthing classes or talk to someone who recently delivered. Our basic lists include:

Dad's List to Bring

- ☐ Folder with important documents – insurance cards, pre-admission forms, birth plan (two or three copies), etc.
- ☐ Baby book (many nurseries will put your baby's footprint in the book).
- ☐ Watch with second hand or digital readout.
- ☐ Change of clothes and pajamas if you are staying overnight.
- ☐ Basic toiletries: toothbrush, shaver, shampoo, deodorant.
- ☐ Comfortable shoes — you may do a lot of walking.
- ☐ Something to read to mom.
- ☐ CD, iPod or other player or small boom box with her favorite music.
- ☐ Pain-easing tools recommended at your birthing classes – tennis balls, hot or cold packs, massagers, lotion, etc.
- ☐ Bathing suit for you — help mom take a shower to ease labor pains.
- ☐ Something for you to eat and drink: sandwich, power bars and juice, in a small cooler; pack snacks for mom and you for after the birth.
- ☐ Cash to have on hand.
- ☐ Pen and pad of paper.
- ☐ Camera (photos and/or video), with extra film, battery, etc.
- ☐ Address book/list of phone numbers to announce the birth.
- ☐ Cell phone or calling card.
- ☐ Champagne — put your name on it, ask a nurse to store it in the fridge.
- ☐ _____
- ☐ _____
- ☐ Childbirth Coaching Guide.

Basics for Her

- ☐ Nightgown and slippers.
- ☐ Her pillow.
- ☐ Socks to keep her feet warm.
- ☐ Hard candies or suckers.
- ☐ Extra magazines.
- ☐ Infant care reference book.
- ☐ Breast feeding guide book.
- ☐ Glasses/contacts and supplies.
- ☐ Outfit for going home along with makeup and hair care.

Basics for Your Baby

- ☐ Outfit for going home (in style).
- ☐ Hat and booties to keep her warm.
- ☐ Mittens so he does not scratch his face.
- ☐ Two or three receiving blankets for swaddling, etc.
- ☐ Diapers (for newborns) and wipes.
- ☐ If necessary, formula and bottles.

 Bring your vitamins with you, or Gatorade, or whatever. I was jamming for three and a half days straight before we got home.
- Veteran Dad

1 Ramping Up

ESSENTIAL CHECKLISTS

Install the Car Seat Early

Install it early and get used to adjusting the straps. National Highway Traffic and Safety Administration recommendations about car-ride safety for your baby are as follows:

1. Use rear-facing convertible or infant-only seat for the first year.
2. Tightly install child seat in car's rear seat, facing the rear (base should not move more than 1 inch).
3. Never use a car seat in a vehicle's front seat that has an air bag.
4. Child seat should recline at approximately a 45 degree angle.
5. Harness strap slots should be at or below the infant's shoulder level. Keep harness straps snug.
6. Place chest clip at infant's armpit level to keep straps in place.
7. If necessary for support, place a rolled towel around your baby's head.

If you need help to get it right, consult seatcheck.org to locate a certified car seat fitting expert near you.

Baby Items Highly Recommended By Dads

As you settle in with your baby, sort out what you have and what you still need. These are sure bets according to Boot Camp veterans:

☐ Diaper Genie – helps eliminate smells.
☐ Bouncy seat (with sound and lights) – entertainment and exercise.
☐ Swing – puts your baby to sleep.
☐ Soft chest carrier - feels great, easily entertained and can put him to sleep.
☐ Battery operated stick-on touch lights – convenient and not too bright for a baby or sleeping spouse.
☐ Digital camera and/or video camera.
☐ Bassinet or cradle – a small moveable alternative to the crib.
☐ Baby bath tub with insert that helps hold newborns.
☐ Stash of diapers, wipes, and diaper rash ointments.
☐ Bathrobe for mom – a nice big, soft one that she will want to wear for weeks.
☐ Big screen TV for a couple that is staying home more often.

Make a List of Things You Like To Do Together Now

As an investment in your relationship, sit down with your wife and make a list of the things you like to do now, before the baby arrives. After life with the baby settles down, pull out the list and pick out something to do. Even if your options are still limited, it will remind you both what you had together, and will make it more likely you will get most of it back.

Final Check List

☐ Keep your cell phone charged to ensure you can be contacted anytime during the day.
☐ Make arrangements with your work in terms of time off, transitioning workload or possibly designating someone to cover your load. If it is possible, avoid traveling.
☐ Have a watch with a second hand to count contractions.
☐ Are you ready for the birth? Review the coaching guide to ensure you know the basics.
☐ Once the baby is born, put a message on your phone answering machine announcing the baby's name, size, time of birth, eye color, etc. Ask callers to leave a message and understand that you are busy and it may be a while before you get back to them.
☐ _____
☐ _____
☐ _____

> **“** *Be sure that when you go to the hospital to pick up mom and baby, you've made a trial run. When my baby was ready to come home I had the car seat but it wasn't installed. I got mom and baby down to the car and found that we weren't prepared for the ride home!* **”**
>
> *- Veteran Dad*

TO DO LIST BEFORE BIRTH

For the Hospital

- ☐ Pre register.
- ☐ Clarify any out-of-pocket costs or limitations on your health insurance.
- ☐ Find out where to park and enter the hospital.
- ☐ Take a tour of the maternity ward; ask a lot of questions.
- ☐ Help your wife prepare a birth plan. (See sample at birthplan.com).
- ☐ Make sure the car is in good shape and keep plenty of gas in the tank.
- ☐ Make a practice driving run to the hospital and install the car seat.

In the house

- ☐ Try and get unfinished projects handled prior to junior's arrival as they can be problematic with a baby in the house.
- ☐ Check out the house for loose railings, outside steps slippery in snow, clutter in hallway, or other safety hazards for a parent carrying a baby.
- ☐ Help your wife set up the nursery or area where your baby will sleep and indulge her "nesting" instinct.
- ☐ Stock it with an ample supply of diapers, wipes, lotions, clothes, etc.
- ☐ Obtain other items on your list(s) of baby equipment and supplies.
- ☐ Clean the bottles and other feeding supplies (as necessary).
- ☐ Stock batteries (nearly all baby related electronics require them).
- ☐ Pre-arrange pet care, if needed.

In General

- ☐ Complete a will or living trust, and consider purchasing life insurance.
- ☐ Take a class on newborn care, Boot Camp for New Dads, First Aid/ CPR, etc.
- ☐ Put the doctor, hospital, and any other important contact numbers in your cell phone address book.
- ☐ Work out general "help" and visit policies for in-laws and friends. (See page 2-C).
- ☐ Pack for the hospital in advance, because your baby may come early.
- ☐ Make a list of everyone you can think of to mail out baby announcements to. Make sure you have registered at a baby store or big department store so people will be able to get you what you want.
- ☐ Register with online sites, such as babycenter.com and you'll not only get great information, you'll also get coupons and discounts on baby stuff.
- ☐ Enjoy as much time with your wife as you can manage, as it might be a while before you are able to do this again.

Nursery Safety

- Be careful with used baby equipment. In some cases these items are unsafe, both because of changing safety guidelines or defects from use (such as missing parts).
- The Juvenile Products Manufacturers Association (JPMA) sponsors a safety-certification program; check for the seal.
- For information on recalled products, call the U.S. Consumer Product Safety Commission hotline at 1-800-638-2772 or visit its website at cpsc.gov
- Blinds with long pull-cords are a hazard, especially looped cords, as a baby can get these wrapped around her neck.

Arrange Time Off Work

If taking weeks of unpaid leave is not an option, consider the following alternatives:

- Work half days, which can stretch out limited time off.
- Take off one midweek day each week for one to two months, which gives you time with your new child and gives mom a break she can plan on over a period of time.
- Ask other recent dads, particularly fellow employees, for their insights and suggestions.
- Ask your HR department or manager about other benefits your company might have.
- Check out your state laws for any other options that might be open to you.

Negotiating With Your Employer

- Try working overtime now in exchange for time off when the baby arrives.
- Talk to your boss in advance about using accrued vacation time.

Preparing Yourself

Becoming a father is a process with ups and downs, and the trick is to get ahead of the curve with a pro-active, constructive approach to the challenges you encounter. Holding and caring for a baby before yours arrives goes a long way. Take advantage of opportunities with babies of friends or relatives, or go visit a new father you know and ask him to show you how he does it. See Section 5 for additional information that will help you prepare.

"Get as much done ahead of time. A big mistake we made was not buying the mini-van before the baby was born. I tell you, going around on weekends with a newborn and talking to salesmen - it's something you really don't want to go through. Get things done early so you can spend more time with your baby."
— Veteran Dad

1 Ramping Up

THOUGHTS ABOUT MY CHILD: A Mini Journal from your Father

Date/Event	Thinking of You/What's Happening

Ramping Up

> *H*er head popped out, her eyes popped open and locked onto mine and "wham!" I was gone. It was incredible.
> *- Veteran Dad*

CONNECT WITH YOUR BABY BEFORE BIRTH

A mother's bond to her baby is hard-wired. We fathers have to build ours from scratch, and we can start early by doing simple things that make him real in our own minds to enable our natural feelings for our child to surface and grow.

- **Track His Amazing Transformation Within Mom**

  The egg transforms into a little tadpole that grows arms and legs and then a heart that starts beating. Amazing stuff, and if you track these changes through pictures, when he arrives, you'll feel like you already know him.

- **Listen to Her Heartbeat**

  Go with mom to her doctor visits. You'll be able to hear your baby's heartbeat at 3 to 4 months with a stethoscope and even earlier with an ultrasound device. It's amazing to actually hear her and listen to a real heartbeat that sounds strong and even powerful for how small she is.

- **See Him in a Sonogram**

  It's a big moment for us guys when we see him for the first time. He's all there and this picture is worth a lot more than words. Get one for your wallet. If you're lucky you might see him move.

- **Feel Her Kick**

  Around 6 months, when mom invites you to put your hand on her tummy, you'll feel your baby move for the first time. Whoa, she's really in there! Later on you'll be shocked by how hard your baby can kick. Spooning in bed with mom is a great way to feel her.

- **Talk to Him & Give Him A Nickname**

  If you make a habit of talking to him in mom's belly, your baby will recognize your voice when you first talk to him after he's born. As he hears and sees you for the first time, he seems to know you are his father. It's a magical moment for you and a real comfort for him in his strange new world.

- **Imagine What You Will Do Together as She Grows**

  If you think about the adventures you want to have together, whether it's teaching her to fish, surf, work on cars or name the stars, you are not only more likely to do these things, but it is a great way to bond as you realize how much you have to look forward to with your child.

- **Buy or Build Something For Her That's Just From You**

  Go out by yourself and pick something meaningful, like her first baseball mitt. If you like working with your hands, you might want to refinish a cradle, or build her a sled, toy box, rocking horse, etc. One guy made up a "diaper bag" using a tool bag. His message: "I am changing her diapers, but as soon as she's out, we're working on stuff together" (a surfing or fishing bag can work, golf bags do not).

- **Imagine Your First Moments with Him**

  Even though he cannot focus clearly, his eyes will be full of curiosity, absorbing this new world that he is seeing for the first time. As you hold him close and say "welcome to the world," he'll respond to your voice, gaze up at you, and see a father who will protect and care for him. Life doesn't get any more real.

- **Write Down a Few Of Your Thoughts About Her**

  Our children love to hear about the great times we had with them growing up, and we forget much more than we ever remember. Even if you do not write much, record your early thoughts about her as you experience the above events (it helps make it real for you as well). Use the mini-journal on the back and pull it out and put it into her baby book as a keepsake she will treasure.

> **❝** *I sang the same song to him 3 times a day. When the cesarean was done and he was on the warmer by himself, I was able to console him by singing that same tune. He knew who I was immediately. And familiarity seemed to calm him down.*
>
> *- Veteran Dad* **❞**

ISSUES TO NOT WORRY ABOUT; A FEW TO PLAN ON

We would like to say "no worries, mate," but the reality is that a man becoming a father has a lot on his mind. Our collective experience and suggestions can help you sort through your issues and get on a constructive track:

Don't Worry About Taking Care of Your Baby

Many men are concerned about taking care of crying babies, changing dirty diapers, etc. In our workshops, even the most nervous guy takes only a few minutes to get used to holding a baby. After just three times changing, feeding, burping, bathing, etc., their own baby, they have it down. While the first days can be harrowing, you will get 80% of it down after two weeks and be an expert on your own baby after four. Check out our baby care tips in Section 3 and watch the guys do it at DadsAdventure. com. You'll quickly realize that you can too.

Don't Worry About Handling Your Baby's Birth

Go ahead and worry about your baby - everyone does. And worrying about your wife being in pain is standard as well. To minimize any concerns about your ability to help her through as her birth coach, we put everything you need to know on a fold-out card like football coaches use to stay on their game plan. Tear it out, put in your hospital bag and you'll do fine.

Think About the New Mom In Your Life

Some new fathers are stunned by a rapid decline in their relationships once the baby arrives; others find theirs flourishing. If you understand how a wife transforms into a mother, and how to support her, work together in raising your baby and bring back the romance, yours will flourish. See Section 4 for what you need to know.

Think the Economics Through

They will change and you need to think them through and respond constructively. In addition to balancing the new family budget, economics includes who works, who cares for the baby, commitments to long commutes or big mortgages, how both you and mom can bring balance to your lives, etc. Big changes may be in order; see pages 5E-F and 7A for tips.

Expect Ambivalence at Times

Expect downs with the ups; you may cry joyfully at her birth and wonder what you got yourself into a week later. This is surprising and runs counter to your expectations, but sleep deprivation, rapid change in your life and the sacrifices you make can overwhelm your feelings for a child you barely know.

Expect To Gain Strength from Your Baby

A child can bring out the best in us and can make us stronger. All of us have issues we would like to handle - from getting a degree to quitting smoking - and when we hold our very immortality in our arms and he smiles at us, motivation to get it done comes easier. The fulfillment you get from being a dad will fuel your drive to do more.

Expect It To Go Fast

A baby comes out of the chute in a rapidly evolving state; this means that if you are not engaged or around, you will miss out and may live to regret it. The worst parts also pass quickly – crying due to colic is generally over by 3 months – although it seems a lot longer.

Advice On All That Advice

If you listen to the "experts," many whom conflict with one another, you'll think that you need a Ph.D. in infant development to take your baby home. And then there are the multitudes, ranging from your mother-in-law to strangers on the streets, who want to tell you whether you will be having a boy or girl, the kinds of foods mom should be eating or how to create a baby genius by 3 months. Take all "advice" with a grain of salt; ultimately, you and your mate will decide what is best for your family.

Expect To "Come Last" For a While

The most distinguishing characteristic of a man who transforms into a dad is that he is no longer self-centered – his priorities shift to his child, mom, work and then himself. Tougher for some than others, this makes the difference between a father and a dad. Do a status check on your priorities occasionally to see how you are doing. (See pages 5-K through 5-N).

Plan To Be Proactive

It is easy to just get swept along in mom's wake on the changes a new baby brings, but you run the risk of being swept in a direction you will regret. Fatherhood is a huge rite of passage for any man, and getting educated, developing a plan and getting involved is a no-brainer. A good place to start – ask yourself what your own father was like and how you want to be.

Everybody says it's going to change your life. OK - well, what does that mean?

- Veteran Dad

WELCOME TO FATHERHOOD: We're Here To Help

We Learned To Do It Our Way

In 1990 we started a workshop with experienced fathers and their babies orienting dads-to-be, and called it Boot Camp for New Dads. We found that dealing with crying babies, crying moms, and the many issues that emerge is a lot easier when you learn what works from dads who have been there and done it.

We wanted to do it our own way, so no women "over 2 feet tall" were allowed. The dads-to-be returned as experienced fathers along with their own babies to orient the next group of guys, and this non-profit expanded across the U.S. and now to England. Over 200,000 men have joined us to learn how to do their best as fathers.

Along the way, research has found that by following our instincts and doing what comes naturally, we dads help our babies grow in unique and essential ways. Doing so turns out to be a great way to raise a family, as mom gets much-appreciated balance in her life and we and our children also have fun.

Today We Have More Opportunity

Today each successive generation of fathers is enjoying a closer connection with their children, and our sons no doubt will raise the bar further. While we face obstacles to being close to our kids (like long work hours or simply not knowing how), we also are riding a wave of support and encouragement from those around us, especially other dads who show us by example. While our own fathers or grandfathers generally got the short end of the stick, for us doors are opening, including the ones many of us go through when we leave work early for our child's soccer game.

We Also Have More Responsibility

We are delivering on our commitment to do our best for our kids, and it is a lot of work. In fact, it is three times the amount of time our fathers put in. Fatherhood has gotten tougher and no matter your circumstances, at some point you will be seriously challenged. Many of you will exhibit a depth of strength and courage you had no idea was inside you. You will be surprised how much of it comes naturally, though you shouldn't be, since for several millennia (until last century's industrial revolution) we all worked out of our homes. Recent research has also found that this ancestry equipped us with biological capabilities that enable us to patiently rock our colicky baby to sleep as well as pull him out of a burning building.

We Definitely Have More Fun

Turns out this is the way it has been for those millennia, and as it is meant to be. Research has found that playing is essential to a baby's full development, and that fathers are babies' natural buddies. Our roughhousing refines their motor skills and confidence, and our inclination to show them the world expands their horizons and teaches them to take risks. The adventure continues with a tour of the hardware store, then some baby wrestling, growing corn with a toddler who loves mud (girls too), fishing with a 2-year old with a plastic fish on her line, and later sharing a passion for surfing or website development, or perhaps climbing mountains together – whatever your future together brings.

We Can Help You Do It Your Way

There are many ways to be a great dad, and we are here to help you find the way that works best for you, not tell you how to do it. The *Crash Course For New Dads* summarizes what we have learned from the many thousands of men who have participated in Boot Camp for New Dads workshops; it is what you need to know to get a great start as a father. Check out DadsAdventure.com for more in-depth information on any issue that concerns you.

We are here to help your do you best as a dad and make fatherhood the adventure of your life. Good luck, and consider us your brothers-(with babies)-in-arms.

DADSADVENTURE.COM
CAN HELP YOU GET A GREAT START

DadsAdventure.com is the supplementary website to *Crash Course for New Dads* and provides what you need to know to thrive as a new father. It presents the perspectives of men who have participated in *Boot Camp for New Dads* as well as related research and information collected over two decades. It is the web's most comprehensive resource for new fathers.

Find In-Depth Supplementary Information To The *Crash Course For New Dads*

Each chapter has a related section on DadsAdventure.com that provides broad, in-depth supplementary information so you can dig into any issue as deeply as you want.

See How-To-Videos Featuring Experienced Dads

Changing diapers, giving baths, calming a crying baby - nothing quite like having another guy show you how in terms you understand to give you the confidence you can do it too. Before long, you will be showing the guys how it is done.

Get What You Need In The New Father Resource Center

No matter what issues you may face as a new father, you can find the help you need in the *New Fathers Resource Center*, the nation's only information and referral system for new fathers.

Get Your Questions Answered By The Experts

Ask any question you want and get answers you can trust from experienced Boot Camp Coaches in the "Ask A Dad" feature, or from other dads in our forums.

Check Out Our Blog For Men Becoming Fathers

You may not have noticed since you are new to fatherhood, but there is a growing fascination with all things baby and mom, and increasingly dad too. We provide the perspective of our dads and it should reflect yours as well.

Get Information On *Boot Camp For New Dads* Workshops In Your Region

Boot Camp for New Dads is acclaimed by virtually all who participate, and if one is located in your community, you will find it enlightening, unique and very worthwhile. For locations, visit DadsAdventure.com or BCND.org.

Find Out How Men Make Fatherhood An Adventure With Their Child

The ultimate experience in fatherhood is to make it an adventure, and the earlier you start, the better. You will find examples of dads and their kids who are having the times of their life that will give you ideas for your own adventure.

Get Downloads Like Dads Adventure Magazine

Dads Adventure magazine is for the dad-to-be, and if you did not get one from your hospital, you can download it from DadsAdventure.com, along with other downloads you will find helpful.

Share What You Have Learned With The Next Guy

Your experience will be valuable to those who follow you, and you can contribute your own insights to help out the next guy. When it comes to raising our children, we dads are all in this together.

Join Us

We are dads helping each other do our best for our kids, and it would be great to have you with us. There is no formal membership; just learning from the men on the job as fathers, and helping out the next guy in line.

WHO WE ARE

My brothers and I grew up taking care of babies. Along with working on cars and fishing for trout, it was just something one did in a family with 13 children. Changing diapers was like cleaning fish; it just went with the territory. So when I became a father myself I knew what to do with our first child, and after four, my friends were asking me for advice on their babies.

I felt most new fathers would enjoy their babies more if they knew what I did, so in 1990, I organized a workshop for dads-to-be at the local hospital. I asked my friends to join me and bring their babies, and for three hours they smiled, slept, cried and did what babies do, and the "rookie" dads-to-be watched us take care of them without a mom in sight. When several said they had never held a baby before, we handed them ours.

We "veterans" talked about our experiences and offered advice, and we all got to know and trust each other. With everything said in the room staying in the room, nothing was left off the table. The rookies went home feeling "I can do this," and they did and returned several months later as veterans with their own babies to orient the next group of rookies.

We call it *Boot Camp for New Dads* (BCND.org), and it has since expanded to 43 states, the U.S. Army, Navy and Air Force, and recently England and Australia. Characterized as a "nursery in a locker room", over 200,000 men have joined us, just regular guys from all walks of life. We help and encourage each other; in a sense, we act like my brothers did.

WHAT WE OFFER YOU

This *Crash Course for New Dads* provides dads-to-be a comprehensive orientation on fatherhood from the real experts – men doing the job as new fathers. We have boiled this information down, along with the best and latest research, into a very concise format you will find easy to use, and backed it up with a website offering in-depth supplementary information.

Including "crash course" and "cheat sheets" in the title may give one the idea it is intended for men who want to take it easy on their road to fatherhood. The opposite is the case; it is intended for men who understand that over the past 2 decades, opportunities as well as the bar for new fathers have risen considerably, and in the few months before their baby arrives, there is a great deal to learn.

There are a variety of tear-out tools like the Childbirth Coaching Guide you will find very useful, including simple ways to record your thoughts as you transform into a dad over the next year. Fatherhood is a journey and it is helpful to periodically take note of where you are in relation to where you started. We also make it easy for you to pass on what you learn as a new father to the next guy to help keep the cycle going.

Please join us in helping each other do our best as fathers. This is our way of making the world a better place for all our children.

Greg Bishop
Founder and Head Coach
Boot Camp for New Dads

CRASH COURSE FOR NEW DADS: Tools, Checklists & Cheat-Sheets

CHILDBIRTH COACHING GUIDE

Childbirth Coaching Guide	A	D	Help Her Deal With Pain
Coaching First Time Moms Through Labor	B	E	Birth Plan Summary
Contraction and Birth Log	C	F	Dad's Magical Moment

1 RAMPING UP TO BIRTH

- A Welcome To Fatherhood: We're Here To Help
- B Issues To Not Worry About; A Few To Plan On
- C Connect With Your Baby Before Birth
- D Thoughts About My Child: A Mini Journal
- E To Do List Before Birth
- F Essential Checklists
- G What You Need For The Hospital
- H Handling an Emergency Birth

2 SETTLING IN WITH YOUR BABY

- A Make The Most Of Your First Day As A Father
- B Helping Mom Breastfeed
- C Getting Settled At Home
- D Strategies For Surviving The First Weeks
- E Support & Emergency Contacts
- F Weekly Survival Chart
- G Weekly Survival Chart
- H Weekly Survival Chart
- I Strategies For Thriving In The First Weeks
- J How To Get Out Of The House

3 CARING FOR A NEW BABY

- A Learning To Care For Your New Baby
- B Milestones For New Dads
- C Great Ways to Bond With Your Baby
- D How Can I Help My Baby Go To Sleep?
- E Troubleshooter's Guide To Crying Babies
- F Ways To Calm A Crying Baby
- G How Your Baby Grows And Develops
- H Show Your Baby The World
- I 1st Year Escapades For Dads & Babies
- J Starting A Life Long Love Affair

4 CARING FOR NEW MOMS

- A How to Support A Mom-To-Be
- B Her Pregnancy By Trimester
- C Her Transformation Into A Mom
- D Caring For a New Mom
- E Help Her Succeed As A Mom
- F Baby Blues & Postpartum Depression
- G Romancing A New Mom
- H Getting Your Love Life Back
- I Dear Moms-To-Be, Love Dads
- J Mom: Help Him Get A Good Start As A Dad

5 TRANSFORMING INTO A DAD

- A Preparing To Become A Father
- B Common Fears & Concerns
- C Research: Our Children Need Us To Be Men
- D Research: Biochemical Changes Help Drive Us Forward
- E Strategies For When Your Time Is Short
- F Options For Balancing Work & Family
- G The Impact of Fatherhood On Men
- H When You Get Overwhelmed Or Close To It
- I How To Transform Into A Dad
- J My Goals As A Father
- K A New Father's Transformation Milestones
- L Get Ahead Of The Curve!
- M New Dad Status Check-Ups
- N Quarterly Status Checks

6 KEEPING HIM SAFE AND HEALTHY

- A Keeping Your Baby Safe
- B When To Baby Proof: Stay Ahead Of The Curve
- C Emergency Medical Instructions
- D Infant CPR & Choking Basics
- E Introducing Pets To Your Baby
- F Child Care Selection Guidelines
- G Preparing For When He Is Sick
- H Understanding Her Symptoms

7 BUILDING A FAMILY

- A Preparing Your Family's Future
- B Family Finance & Administration
- C Recording Your New Family
- D Creating Traditions & Memories
- E Learning More/Getting Help
- F Learning More/Getting Help II
- G Babies With Special Needs
- H Making A Family With A Special Baby

8 MAKING IT AN ADVENTURE

- A Make Your Fatherhood An Adventure
- B Other Dads Show You How
- C 10 Adventures For 0 To 3 Months
- D The 20 Best Tips From Boot Camp For New Dads
- E Great Advice From Experienced Fathers
- F Final Words Of Wisdom From The Guys
- G We Are All In This Together
- H Welcome To Serious Manhood

1 Ramping Up
2 Settling In
3 Caring for Baby
4 Caring for Mom
5 Transforming
6 Safe & Healthy
7 Family
8 Adventure

Crash Course for New Dads

Published by

Dads Adventure
15375 Barranca Pkwy., Suite H-104
Irvine, CA   92618

Cover Design – Kristen Loewe
Page Layout - David Moses
Illustrations – Jason Davis

Library of Congress Control Number – 2007907538
ISBN – 13   978-0-9727829-3-7
ISBN – 10   0-9727829-3-1

Information and advice in this book has been carefully researched and every effort has been made to ensure accuracy. Although health care professionals have reviewed pertinent chapters, this book should never substitute for the advice of your personal physician. *Dads Adventure* assumes no responsibility for any damages or losses incurred as a result of following the information contained herein.

Official website: DadsAdventure.com

CRASH COURSE FOR NEW DADS:

Tools, Checklists & Cheat-Sheets

200,000 New Fathers - The Real Experts

Tell You What You Need To Know

Greg Bishop

Head Coach, Boot Camp for New Dads

DadsAdventure.com   Irvine, CA